RECORDING GREAT AUDIO

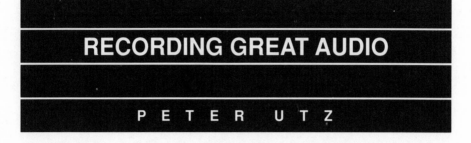

RECORDING GREAT AUDIO

PETER UTZ

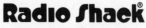

Radio Shack®
A Division of Tandy Corporation
Fort Worth, TX 76102

ACKNOWLEDGMENTS

We wish to thank the following for providing the photographs as listed.

Courtesy of Radio Shack, A Division of Tandy Corporation: pp. 9–11, 17, 19 (bottom), 22–23, 40, 46 (top), 69–70, 114, 117–20, and 126.

Courtesy of R.D. Systems of Canada, Division of GELECO ELECTRONICS LTD.: p. 16.

First edition published February 1989.

Produced for Radio Shack, A Division of Tandy Corporation
Fort Worth, Texas

Published by Quantum Publishing, Inc.
Mendocino, California 95460
Copyright © 1989 Quantum Publishing, Inc.

ISBN 0-930633-15-6

To my cat, Tinkle, who kept his claws out of my notes and his hairs out of my disk drives long enough for me to finish this manuscript.

CONTENTS

CHAPTER 1

THE SCIENCE OF SOUND

Here's a mini science lesson just to get us started. When an object vibrates, it wiggles air molecules nearby (unless you are standing on the moon). Those molecules move their neighbors and the neighbors move more distant neighbors. In this way, a wave travels from a vibrating object to your ear. The jiggling molecules then agitate your eardrum and you hear sound.

Sound can be described by its pitch and its loudness. When something vibrates at a high FREQUENCY, it has a high pitch like a bird tweet. Foghorns and tubas, on the other hand, create low-FREQUENCY sounds. When we are young, our ears can hear notes as low as 20 vibrations per second or 20 cycles per second or 20 HERTZ (Hz) and as high as 20,000 vibrations per second or 20 KILOHERTZ (kHz). Frequencies lower than 20 Hz or higher than 20 kHz can sometimes be felt but are not heard (except by some animals). As we grow older, our frequency response (along with other responses) fades out. Older people often lose their ability to hear the higher frequencies of the letters s, t, and other consonants. There is the story of the old man who proudly told his friend that he had gotten a new hearing aid. "What kind is it?" his friend asked. "Oh, about three o'clock," the old man replied.

Table 1-1 lists some common frequency ranges. Notice how few devices will reproduce the entire audible spectrum. You can also see why frequency modulation (FM) radio sounds better than amplitude modulation (AM) radio and why telephones sound tinny.

The loudness or volume of sound is measured in DECIBELS (dB). Table 1-2 compares the loudness of common sounds. The DECIBEL scale is logarithmic, which means that when you go up 3 dB in sound level, you are doubling the volume of the sound. Thus, measured on a meter, 103 dB is twice as loud as 100 dB. If you think the dB scale is weird, the ear is even weirder. Although the human ear is capable of hearing a 1-dB increase in sound under laboratory conditions, it takes a 6- to 10-dB increase in sound level (about four to ten times the actual power of the sound) before your *ear* perceives a doubling in the volume. See Table 1-2 for decibel levels of various noises compared with their perceived sound volumes.

You will see DECIBELS mentioned time and again when equipment and volume levels are described, so it is good to get a feel for what the numbers mean. Just remember this:

- 3 dB doubles the power of the sound, but it only seems a little louder.
- 10 dB multiplies the sound power tenfold, but it only seems twice as loud to your ear.

TABLE 1-1   Audio frequency ranges

Healthy young ears	20 Hz to 20,000 Hz
Old ears	50 Hz to 10,000 Hz
FM radio (maximum capability)	50 Hz to 15,000 Hz
Most hi-fi equipment under $300	30 Hz to 16,000 Hz
Quality audiocassette player	50 Hz to 15,000 Hz
Table model TV	150 Hz to 10,000 Hz
Portable AM/FM radio	120 Hz to 12,000 Hz
AM radio (maximum capability)	80 Hz to 5,000 Hz
Telephone	300 Hz to 3,000 Hz
Human singing voice	70 Hz to 1,100 Hz
Hi-fi VCR	20 Hz to 20,000 Hz
CD player	20 Hz to 20,000 Hz
Inexpensive microphone	80 Hz to 12,000 Hz
LP records	40 Hz to 20,000 Hz
Lowest note on an organ	16 Hz

The amazing human ear can hear leaves rustle at 1 dB yet can withstand a jet takeoff at 140 dB, where the sound volume is actually ten million times stronger. Loud sound is not good for your ears, however. Thirty-year-old rock musicians often have the hearing of seventy-year olds because the loud music has damaged their auditory nerve endings. Rock concerts, discos, and headphones turned up to "french fry" will unequivocally damage your hearing. According to the U.S. government Occupational Safety and Health Act (OSHA), thirty minutes is all your ears can take at 110 DECIBELS. You can take two hours at 100 DECIBELS or four hours at 95 DECIBELS before your ears begin to self-destruct. It is easy to turn a Walkman up to 100 DECIBELS.

There is more to sound than just loudness and pitch. There's ECHO and REVERBERATION, which we hear when sounds bounce off other things on the way to our ears. ECHO and REVERBERATION give a certain tone to the room (aptly called ROOM TONE), a special "color" or "feel" that tells you where the sound originated. You can tell the difference between a recording made in a classroom from one made in a concert hall from one made in a snowbank from one made in the hull of an empty oil tanker.

ECHOES and REVERBERATION "muddy up" the sound and are generally undesirable. That's often the reason amateur audio recordings sound so bad: they were made in a room with too many echoes.

TABLE 1-2   Loudness in sound volume compared with decibels (dB)

Apparent loudness	Comparative power of the sound volume	dB	
		220	12' in front of cannon below muzzle
		200	
Deafening		180	Rocket engines
		160	Jet engine, close up
		150	Permanent damage to hearing
	10,000,000 ——	140	Loud rock music
	—— 3,162,000 ——	130	Airport runway
	1,000,000 ——	120	Threshold of pain; disco music; thunder
	316,200 ——	110	Power tools; orchestral climax
Very loud	100,000 ——	100	Subway
	31,620 ——	90	Heavy truck traffic
	—— 10,000 ——	80	
Loud	3,162 ——	70	Busy street
	—— 1,000 ——	60	Average conversation
	316 ——	50	Average office
Moderate	100 ——	40	Subdued conversation
	—— 32 ——	30	Quiet office
Faint	10 ——	20	Quiet living room
	3 ——	10	Whisper
Very faint	—— 1 ——	0	Threshold of hearing

Background noise is another part of every room's personality. Everywhere you go (except soundproof studios), there is the faint tick of clocks, hum of motors, squeak of floors, or rumble of wind or jet planes. When recording sound, you want the least amount of background noise possible as it may also obscure your main sound.

Professionals go to great lengths to record in noise-free, echo-free environments. Later, they can introduce electronic REVERBERATION and background sound effects to make their recordings sound natural.

Just as you can get noise and echoes in a room, you can get noise and DISTORTION from your microphones, amplifiers, speakers, and recording equipment. The hum from poor wiring and shielding added to the background hiss of your tape recorder added to the DISTORTION as the sound comes out of your loudspeaker—all conspire to destroy your sound quality. High fidelity means true to life: your sound should come out of your system exactly the way it went in. The unfaithful reproduction of sound makes it possible for you to tell whether the radio is playing or whether someone is singing in your living room. This book will help you achieve high-fidelity sound as you record and play back speeches and music.

Continuing with the science lesson, let's look at how the electronic devices change sound vibrations into electrical signals for recording or playback through loudspeakers.

Microphones contain tiny DIAPHRAGMS much like your eardrums. Sound vibrations wiggle the DIAPHRAGM, which creates a tiny electric current that vibrates at the same rate as the original sound. Thus, for each vibration of sound, there is a tiny electrical vibration carried along the wire from the microphone to the amplifier.

The amplifier, powered by alternating current (ac), the kind that comes from your wall outlet, or direct current (dc), the kind that comes from batteries, strengthens the electrical signal. The amplifier sends a strong electrical signal to speakers that contain ELECTROMAGNETS, coils of wire that move when an electrical signal passes through them. The ELECTROMAGNET, or VOICE COIL, is attached to the SPEAKER DIAPHRAGM, or CONE. Thus electrical vibrations from the amplifier become vibrations in the SPEAKER CONE, making sound you can hear. Think of the speaker as a microphone in reverse. Sound vibrations wiggle the DIAPHRAGM in the microphone making electricity, and electricity wiggles the DIAPHRAGM in the speaker making sound vibrations. By turning the volume control up or down in your amplifier, you strengthen or weaken the electrical signals to the speakers, making them vibrate more vigorously or more gently.

We can record these vibrations for later playback by sending electrical vibrations from an amplifier to a tape recorder. In the tape recorder is a RECORD HEAD, an ELECTROMAGNET that can convert electrical vibrations into magnetic vibrations. The tape recorder slides a ribbon of magnetizable tape over the RECORD HEAD, magnetizing the tape. Thus, the sound vibrations are changed to electrical vibrations, which are then changed to magnetic vibrations that are stored on the tape.

When the tape is played back, it again slides over another ELECTROMAGNET in the tape recorder, called the PLAYBACK HEAD. The PLAYBACK HEAD senses the changing magnetism on the tape and converts it into a weak electrical signal. The signal goes to an amplifier, gets stronger, and comes out a speaker. Thus, the stored magnetic vibrations can be turned into an electrical signal that eventually becomes sound.

Records have a groovy way of storing sound. The record maker sends electrical vibrations to an electromagnet that wiggles a needle as it scrapes a groove in a rotating record. Every sound vibration turns into an electrical vibration, which turns into a needle vibration that leaves a tiny squiggle in the groove. This master record is then duplicated. When the copy is played back, another needle sits in the record groove following the groove's wiggly path. Each vibration shakes the needle that sticks into the PHONOGRAPH CARTRIDGE, which generates a tiny electric current that when amplified can be sent to a speaker and turned into sound vibrations.

In the process of recording and playback, a hundred things can go wrong . . . go wrong . . . go wrong. If the tape machine doesn't pull the tape smoothly over the head, the vibrations get jumbled. Sometimes the tape has some magnetic vibrations already on it that leave noise when the tape is played back. Sometimes the tape stretches, causing the vibrations to stretch a little and come out at the wrong frequency. Sometimes the tape recorder or record player motor doesn't run at a constant speed (maybe the belts or pulleys inside are slipping), causing the pitch of your music to waver. If it wavers slowly, it is called WOW, and if it warbles quickly, like someone was shaking the singer, it is called FLUTTER. Background tape noise is often called HISS because that's what it sounds like.

If you shout too loudly into the microphone, your machinery, unable to register the loud volume, may cause the signal to DISTORT. On the other hand, if your volume is too low, there won't be enough sound to record. If you then turn your sound way up to play it back at a listenable volume, you would also be turning up the undesirable noises in your sound system, such as HISS, HUM, and other garbage.

The purpose of this book is to discover ways of preserving the good sound while keeping the gremlins away. We will be using the science of sound in each step of the process. Audio people, an odd combination of scientists and artists, need to know not only how to make things sound pretty but how to capture the sounds in full detail. For this, they need to be masters of their tools.

MICROPHONES

If you are making audio, then somewhere along the line you are probably using a microphone. In most cases, you can use any microphone whose plug will fit into your recorder's socket. Audio gourmets and serious recordists use more specialized microphones to achieve not just adequate sound but excellent sound.

Microphones change sound into electrical signals in a variety of ways; microphones can also "listen" in various directions. You can make microphones work with different kinds of wires or mate with different kinds of amplifiers. When a microphone's signal doesn't match the amplifier's (or the plugs don't fit), there are adapters and transformers to wed the two. Before diving into the details on how to do this, join me for another science lesson.

HOW MICROPHONES WORK

Sound vibrations enter the microphone and vibrate a diaphragm that generates a weak electrical signal. This signal travels down a wire into a sensitive MICROPHONE INPUT of an AUDIO AMPLIFIER (Figure 2-1).

Some amplifiers' inputs aren't sensitive enough to "hear" the tiny signals from a microphone, so you must use a PREAMPLIFIER (or PREAMP). The PREAMP strengthens the weak electrical signals from the microphone, making them strong enough to feed other audio devices such as AMPLIFIERS.

KINDS OF MICROPHONES

A microphone's sound quality is generally measured by its FREQUENCY RESPONSE—its capability of reproducing a range of audio frequencies. The better, more expensive microphones have a wide FREQUENCY RESPONSE, meaning they are equally sensitive to low, medium, and high tones. A microphone with an 88-Hz to 12,000-Hz response is not as good as one with a 40-Hz to 17,000-Hz response. The second microphone picks up both lower and higher tones than the first.

Professional microphones are often described using a graph to show how sensitive a microphone is at various frequencies (see Figure 2-2). The "perfect" microphone would create a straight line from 20 Hz to 20,000 Hz, representing a FLAT FREQUENCY RESPONSE across the entire spectrum. Normal microphones are FLAT over a certain range and go to pieces at the high and low ends; this is called ROLL-OFF. Other peaks

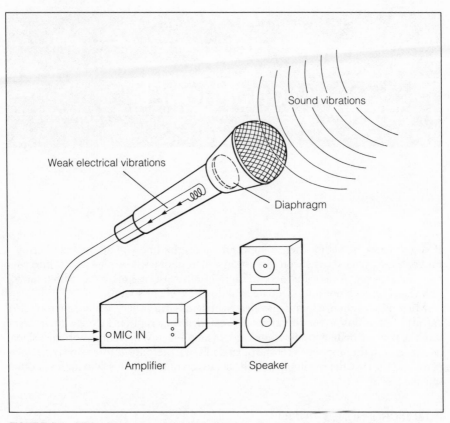

Sound vibrations

Weak electrical vibrations

Diaphragm

○ MIC IN

Amplifier

Speaker

FIGURE 2-1 Microphone converts sound vibrations to weak electrical vibrations

and valleys in the graph show the mike more sensitive to some frequencies and less sensitive to others. A 10-dB dip in the graph line represents a 10-dB drop in power when the mike is reproducing that frequency, cutting the *perceived* loudness in half. The more jagged and humpy the graph line, the less desirable the mike because it will color the sound with its favorite frequencies. A hump at the top of the graph will make a microphone sound shrill, a hump in the middle of the graph (common with cheap mikes) makes it sound tinny, and a hump near the bottom with a dip near the top would make it sound muffled. (See Figure 2-2).

Some microphones are more sensitive than others, which means they will pick up sounds others can't "hear." Microphone sensitivity, usually measured in minus dB, tells how much electrical signal the mike makes for a given volume of sound. A common microphone sensitivity would be –58 dB, whereas a more sensitive microphone might have an output of –48 dB. These numbers don't really matter much except when you wish to pick up very weak sounds like wild cockatoos 30 yards away.

Electret Condenser

The best microphone at the lowest price is probably an ELECTRET CONDENSER mike. Sound vibrations shake a diaphragm in the microphone next to a charged capacitor.

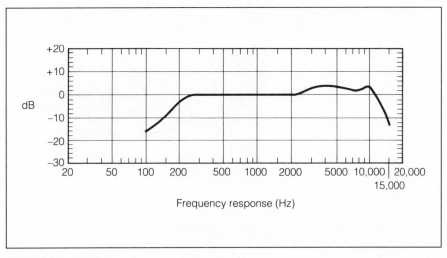

FIGURE 2-2   Microphone frequency response

A battery-powered electric circuit in the microphone senses the movement of the capacitor's electrical charges and sends these electrical vibrations down the wire.

ELECTRET CONDENSER mikes have a wider, flatter FREQUENCY RESPONSE than their DYNAMIC brothers, and do so at a reasonable cost. They are lightweight and can be very small (handy for tiny LAPEL CLIP microphones). Figure 2-3 shows a $20 ELECTRET mike.

One disadvantage of the ELECTRET CONDENSER mike is that the battery always seems to be dead when you need it most (probably because you forgot to turn the ON/OFF switch OFF when you finished using it). Also, ELECTRETS are more fragile than their DYNAMIC brothers. You can't get them wet or leave their batteries in for months on end because they could leak and corrode your mike's innards.

FIGURE 2-3
Electret condenser
microphone

FIGURE 2-4
Dynamic microphone

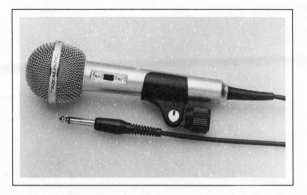

The grandfather of the ELECTRET CONDENSER microphone is the professional studio CONDENSER microphone. These expensive high quality mikes require a separate power supply (not just a battery) to work.

Dynamic

If you are working in rugged or humid environments or are tired of replacing batteries, then you may wish to switch to the slightly more expensive DYNAMIC microphone. These mikes sense sound using a magnet and a coil of wire and thus require no batteries. Good ones cost $150 and up. The less expensive models are a bit weak in the low frequencies. Figure 2-4 shows a $22 model. DYNAMIC mikes may also have ON/ OFF switches to silence the mike when it is not in use.

Crystal, Ceramic, and Carbon

CRYSTAL and CERAMIC mikes cost about five dollars and go with portable audiocassette recorders. They generally put out a strong signal and are okay for voice but otherwise have terrible fidelity, especially in the bass frequencies. Avoid them. The CARBON mike is used in telephones and radio headsets to pick up speech only. It has terrible frequency response but is cheap and extremely rugged.

Pressure Zone

The PRESSURE-ZONE microphones (PZM) are built into a flat plate (see Figure 2-5). They are moderately expensive (about $50 and up), yield a fairly wide FREQUENCY RESPONSE, and do a fair job of rejecting echoes. They are excellent for picking up a poker party (simply place the mike in the center of the table) or for picking up the kid's Christmas play (set the microphone at the edge of the stage).

Stereo

When you are recording stereophonic sound, you could use either two microphones or one microphone with two sound sensors in it. It is not easy to set up two microphones to capture stereo sound that also sounds good when played back on monaural equipment. STEREO mikes simplify the process by providing stereo sound in one easy hookup.

FIGURE 2-5
PZM microphone

The double mike records both the right and the left channels and sends the signals down a cable to a stereo mike plug. Most camcorders today are stereo and equipped to handle such a plug. In fact, if your camcorder has a stereo mike jack and you plug a monaural extension mike into it, you might be recording on only one channel. This won't hurt anything, but it takes advantage of only half your stereo sound system's capabilities. To use a monaural mike with your stereo videocassette recorder (VCR), pick up from Radio Shack or some other electrogadget store, a MONO-TO-STEREO adapter, which takes the mono signal and sends it equally to both stereo channels. The adapter won't make stereo sound, but it will at least fill both channels with the same sound, resulting in fuller sound.

STEREO mikes, like the one in Figure 2-6, cost around $24 to $40. Professional models cost over $1,000 (better send Santa a candygram if you want this one).

Wireless

A WIRELESS microphone sends its signal to an FM radio transmitter. The signal is then picked up by a special FM receiver or, in the less expensive systems, can be tuned in

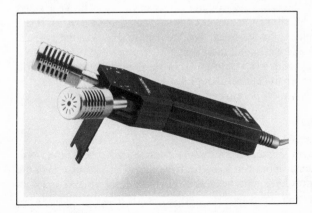

FIGURE 2-6
Stereo microphone

by any FM radio. The WIRELESS mike allows you to travel around an area unencumbered by tangles of microphone cable. With camcorders this means your performer can travel freely up to perhaps 100 feet from you while the receiver on your camcorder picks up the sound loud and clear.

One disadvantage of WIRELESS mikes is that radio interference, signal reflections, and metal obstacles can mess your FM signal causing a hiss or whoosh in the background or, in some cases, your sound just cuts out. The higher-quality, more-expensive FM mikes ($100–$2,000) have better transmitters and receivers that reduce this undesirable effect. The $1,000-plus models have dual antennas and receivers so that if one antenna can't receive a signal, the other antenna generally will, leaving you with a strong clear signal most of the time.

Some WIRELESS mikes have their transmitters built right into the microphone body. The antenna is a little tail hanging off the bottom of the mike; you just turn the mike on and blab. With other models you can use any mike you choose (perhaps a LAPEL mike), plugging this mike into the transmitter that you've stuffed in your pocket or taped to your body.

Tie Clip, Lapel Clip, and Lavalier

These tiny mikes clip to a tie or a lapel or hang around your neck. They are OMNIDIRECTIONAL (explained shortly) and should be placed about six inches below the mouth. Because of the loud bassy vibrations of the chest, the mikes have weak bass FREQUENCY RESPONSE and strong treble FREQUENCY RESPONSE. Thus, do not hang a regular mike around somebody's neck with a string because it will sound bassy. Conversely, a LAVALIER mike, if handheld, will sound tinny.

MICROPHONE PICKUP PATTERNS

Microphones "listen" in various directions. *Omni* means "all," so an OMNIDIRECTIONAL microphone listens in all directions. Other types of microphones are DIRECTIONAL and listen in one or more particular directions.

Microphones are often described by their PICKUP PATTERNS—the directions in which they listen best. Thus by calling a microphone an OMNI or a CARDIOID, you can tell how a microphone picks up sound. A microphone's PICKUP PATTERN may be described graphically (see Figure 2-7). Zero degrees on the diagram represents straight out of the head of the microphone; 180 degrees represents the tail of the microphone. The microphone in Figure 2-7 listens very well in front of it, pretty well to the sides, and not so well behind it (−10-dB sensitivity as opposed to 0-dB sensitivity). If the pattern were a perfect circle, then we would be looking at an OMNIDIRECTIONAL microphone that listens equally well in all directions.

Some mikes allow you to select a PICKUP PATTERN by removing the HEAD (the top part) from the BODY (the handle part) of the microphone and switching it with another HEAD. This way one expensive microphone can do several different jobs.

Omnidirectional

OMNIDIRECTIONAL microphones (Figures 2-3 and 2-4) listen equally in all directions. You don't have to point the microphone at someone to pick up their sounds. OMNIs are good microphones for nonprofessionals because you don't have to pay a lot of attention to aiming or to whether performers are talking directly into the microphone.

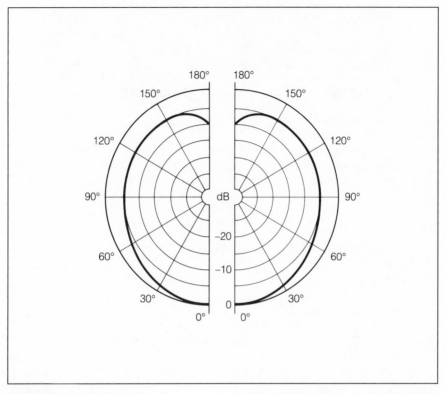

FIGURE 2-7   Polar diagram

Unfortunately, OMNIs also pick up unwanted background sounds. If a reporter is speaking into an OMNI mike while a jet plane is flying overhead, I give you three roaring guesses what you'll hear. Less obvious is the background sound an OMNI picks up from squeaky chairs, rustling papers on the desk, slamming doors, and especially room echoes. OMNIs work fine if used up close because the nearby person or instrument is far louder than the background sounds, making them go unnoticed.

Directional and Unidirectional

DIRECTIONAL and UNIDIRECTIONAL are general terms indicating that the microphone has greater sensitivity in one direction than in others. DIRECTIONAL microphones are good for picking up small groups when you want everyone to be heard but don't want room echoes and other background sounds. Some specific DIRECTIONAL microphones are the SHOTGUN, CARDIOID, HYPERCARDIOID, SUPERCARDIOID, BIDIRECTIONAL, and NOISE CANCELING. Figure 2-8 compares the PICKUP PATTERNS of some of these beasts.

DIRECTIONAL microphones do have one strange property, the PROXIMITY EFFECT. If you move a DIRECTIONAL mike too close to a musical instrument or person, the sound will become exaggerated and bassy, with the low notes too strong and easily heard breath sounds. Bring such a mike within a few inches of your lips and p's and b's will sound like thunderous explosions. OMNIDIRECTIONAL microphones are resistant to this and are thus better for people who cannot keep their kissers off the microphone.

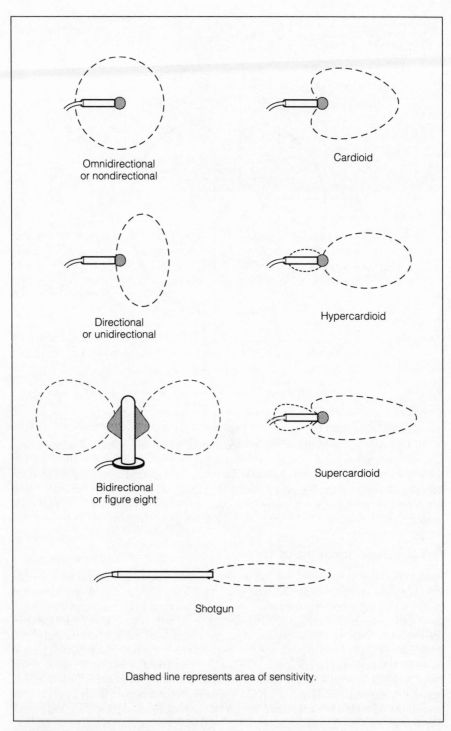

Omnidirectional
or nondirectional

Cardioid

Directional
or unidirectional

Hypercardioid

Bidirectional
or figure eight

Supercardioid

Shotgun

Dashed line represents area of sensitivity.

FIGURE 2-8 Microphone pickup patterns

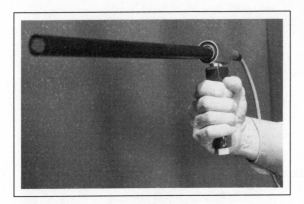

FIGURE 2-9
Shotgun mike with handheld
shock mount

UNIDIRECTIONAL mikes can be thought of as "very DIRECTIONAL"—more sensitive in one direction—which allows you to hold the mike farther from your performer and still pick up the sound. This may be handy for keeping the microphone out of your picture while making a video recording. If you misaim a UNIDIRECTIONAL mike, however, or if the person moves or turns his head, the sound volume will drop noticeably.

Shotgun   Figure 2-9 shows a SHOTGUN microphone, named because of its shape. A very UNIDIRECTIONAL microphone that rejects with extreme prejudice all sounds except those coming from where it is pointed, a SHOTGUN works well in noisy environments, in rooms with lots of echoes, and in situations where you have to record sound from some distance away (like in video).

SHOTGUN mikes don't *magnify* sound: a weak sound remains a weak sound; SHOTGUNS simply *reject* noises coming from the sides and rear. If you want to pick up weak and distant sounds, you may need a PARABOLIC microphone.

Parabolic   Figure 2-10 shows a PARABOLIC mike. This contraption is actually a conventional mike mounted at the focal point of a large parabolic reflector. Because the reflector funnels sound to the microphone, the mechanism is very sensitive and can often pick up people's conversation a block away (a great way to eavesdrop on the parkers at Lovers' Lane). You often see PARABOLICS at football games picking up the grunts, groans, and crushing blows of the players.

PARABOLIC microphones have a fairly poor bass response. Also, they pick up the sounds of distant cars, wind, and snorts and shuffles of the person aiming the mike. Avoid mike operators with runny noses.

Cardioid   CARDIOID mikes look like OMNIs, although some have a sleeker design without a ball on the end. CARDIOIDs get their name from their heart-shaped POLAR PATTERN (see Figures 2-7 and 2-8), which allows a person to speak about 18 inches or so from the microphone without having the microphone pick up too many room echoes. More forgiving than the UNIDIRECTIONAL microphone, it allows a person to move his face or the microphone without losing much sound volume.

Like turtles and armadillos, CARDIOIDs have very insensitive backsides, making them good for cutting out the audience or crowd sounds, room echoes, or feedback from loudspeakers in the room. (We will discuss feedback later.)

FIGURE 2-10
Parabolic mike

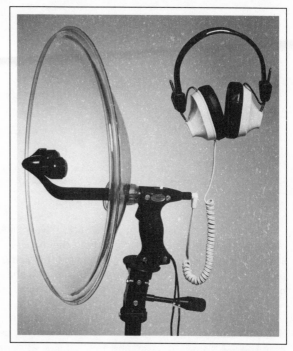

Hypercardioid and Supercardioid   HYPERCARDIOID and SUPERCARDIOID are variations of the CARDIOID microphone that are more UNIDIRECTIONAL. They can also be used a little farther away from the performer (up to 4 feet). Unlike most other mikes, they yield good bass at this distance. In fact, if too close to the performer, the bass will become overbearing.

Noise Canceling   Use NOISE-CANCELING microphones where background noise is extremely loud, such as in a helicopter or on a crowded convention floor. Often built into headsets with a microphone positioned directly in front of the speaker's mouth, they are not renowned for great fidelity, but generally speech is all you are trying to pick up from them anyway.

MICROPHONE IMPEDANCE

IMPEDANCE is an electronic term that describes how a microphone and its wires transfer signals to the circuits in the amplifier or tape recorder. IMPEDANCE is measured in OHMS (Ω). HIGH IMPEDANCE (HI-Z) is about 20,000 ohms, and LOW IMPEDANCE (LO-Z) is 100–600 ohms.

Microphones have an IMPEDANCE (usually stamped on them somewhere) and so do the audio inputs and outputs of tape recorders, mixers, and VCRs. LOW-IMPEDANCE equipment is designed to work with other LOW-IMPEDANCE equipment; the same is true for HIGH-IMPEDANCE gear, which means that you shouldn't plug a HIGH-IMPEDANCE microphone into a LOW-IMPEDANCE audio input. You won't hurt the machinery, you'll just get tinny or weak sound.

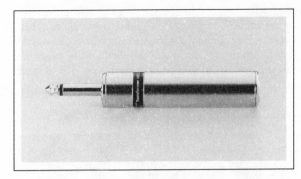

FIGURE 2-11
Low- to high-impedance
adapter

Surprisingly, if you connect a LOW-IMPEDANCE mike to a HIGH-IMPEDANCE audio input, you still get excellent sound. You *cannot*, however, connect a HIGH-IMPEDANCE source into a LOW-IMPEDANCE input; it will sound terrible.

What happens if you are stuck with a HIGH-IMPEDANCE mike and a LOW-IMPEDANCE audio input? All is not lost; just buy an IMPEDANCE MATCHING TRANSFORMER or IMPEDANCE ADAPTER that changes the signal from one to the other. Figure 2-11 shows one of these little $9 gizmos.

Small, inexpensive audio devices are usually high impedance (HI-Z). Large, expensive professional audio gear is generally low impedance (LO-Z). Many microphones and mixers have HI-/LO-Z switches that enable them to work with either HI-Z or LO-Z equipment. Because both LO-Z and HI-Z sources can work with HI-Z audio inputs, most audio equipment has HI-Z audio inputs.

The same laws also apply to connecting audio devices together. You can connect a HI-Z output to a HI-Z input, and you can connect a LO-Z output to either a LO-Z or a HI-Z input. You just cannot connect a HI-Z device to a LO-Z input.

Generally, if a device has a three-pin plug (see the CANON plug and socket shown in Figure 2-12), it is LOW IMPEDANCE. If the plug has only two metal parts, like the MINI, PHONE, and RCA (also called PHONO) plugs in Figure 2-12, the device is HIGH IMPEDANCE.

BALANCED AND UNBALANCED LINES

A mike wire can carry its signal to its destination two ways—BALANCED and UNBALANCED LINES. Home and semiprofessional audio equipment uses UNBALANCED LINES such as the PATCH CORD shown in Figure 2-13. These cables are made with two wires: a thin center conductor that carries the signal and a woven shield wire that encircles it. The shield is a ground wire that keeps interference (like hum and buzz) from entering the cable and infecting your sound. These inexpensive wires usually have two-conductor plugs on the ends, such as a MINI, PHONE, or RCA (see Figure 2-12).

The mikes, plugs, and wires for UNBALANCED systems are inexpensive and simple to maintain. They are adequate for carrying signals the short distance between mixers, audiocassette decks, and nearby amplifiers. Nonprofessional microphones with short cords also may use UNBALANCED LINES.

The problem with UNBALANCED LINES is that they tend to pick up hum, radio interference, and noise from nearby motors. The longer the cable, the more interference you pick up, so keep UNBALANCED LINES to a maximum of 10 feet.

The higher-quality BALANCED LINE has two conductors inside a woven metal shield, making a total of three wires for the cable. The plug at the end of the cable has three pins and a CANON (also called XLR or A3M) connector (review Figure 2-12). BALANCED LINES can carry signals 100 feet or more yet pick up very little stray electrical interference. Most professional and industrial audio equipment uses the higher-quality BALANCED LINES.

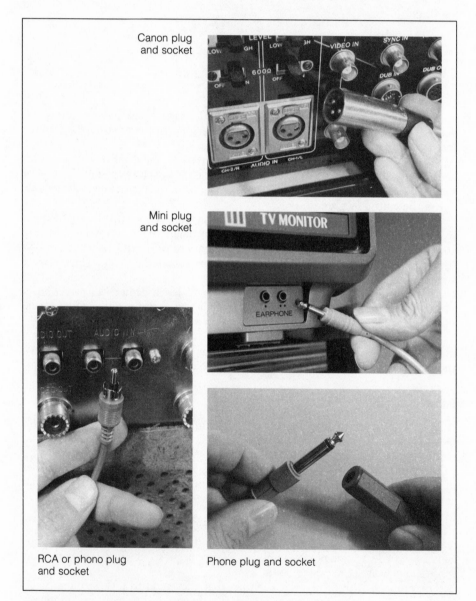

Canon plug and socket

Mini plug and socket

RCA or phono plug and socket

Phone plug and socket

FIGURE 2-12 Various audio plugs

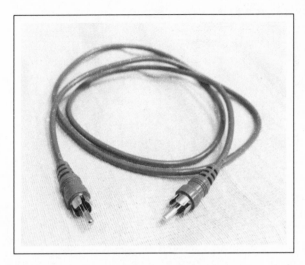

FIGURE 2-13
Audio patch cord uses unbalanced lines

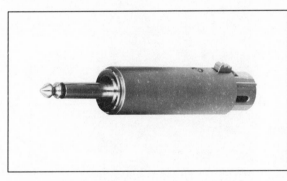

FIGURE 2-14
Adapter converts unbalanced line to balanced line and vice versa

So how do you connect your "professional" mike with its BALANCED LINE and XLR plug to your home VCR or mixer with its UNBALANCED PHONE microphone input? As you might guess, you use an ADAPTER like the one shown in Figure 2-14. The ADAPTER contains a transformer that changes the three-wire BALANCED system to a two-wire UNBALANCED system. This ADAPTER is called a LINE MATCHING TRANSFORMER.

Like insects and wet paint, BALANCED systems and LOW IMPEDANCE are often found together. LOW-IMPEDANCE microphones frequently use BALANCED LINES because LOW-IMPEDANCE microphones are generally professional quality and BALANCED LINES are used on professional equipment. Conversely, cheapie microphones tend to be HIGH IMPEDANCE and use UNBALANCED LINES. If this boggles your mind, study Figure 2-15. Notice that there are many situations where we need to convert from LOW-IMPEDANCE BALANCED LINES to HIGH-IMPEDANCE UNBALANCED LINES. Adapters that do both of these jobs at once contain special transformers that change BALANCED LOW-IMPEDANCE signals to UNBALANCED HIGH-IMPEDANCE signals and vice versa. When buying adapters, make sure you know what kinds of plugs and sockets you are dealing with so a single adapter can make all the conversions at once.

Type of plug	Used with balanced or unbalanced lines	Used with HI-Z or LO-Z mike	Equipment
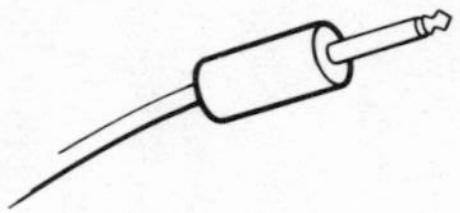 Mini plug	Unbalanced	Usually HI-Z	Audiocassette tape recorders; home VCRs; small portable equipment
 Phone plug	Unbalanced	Usually HI-Z	Home VCRs; reel-to-reel audiotape recorders; most school AV equipment
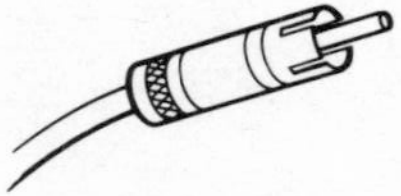 RCA or phono plug	Unbalanced	Usually HI-Z	Musical equipment like guitar amplifiers; some home VCRs; nearly all phono turntables and audiocassette decks
 XLR, A3M, or Canon plug	Balanced	Usually LO-Z	Professional VCRs; most mike mixers and other audio equipment of high quality; nearly all good microphones

FIGURE 2-15 What goes with what

PLUGS AND ADAPTERS

Portable equipment generally uses MINI PLUGS because they're small; larger equipment often uses PHONE (also called 1/4" PHONE) plugs and jacks (sockets) because they're sturdy and inexpensive. Most connections from machine to machine use RCA plugs and jacks; professional audio equipment generally uses XLR plugs and sockets. Murphy's 27th Law—the plug from one device will never match the socket on the other device—means you will forever be buying ADAPTERS to jump from one kind of connector to another. *This is a fact of life*, so take a deep breath and get ready to learn the names of all the plugs and sockets so that you can identify the adapter you need when you get to the store. If you call these things widgets, whatsits, and whatchamacallits, no one will ever take you seriously as an audio expert.

Adapters are named for the kinds of plugs and sockets they have. Plugs, which have a part that sticks out, are male; sockets and jacks, which have a hole, are female. So, for instance, if you have an RCA plug that you can't fit into a MINI socket, you need an adapter that will accept an RCA female and have a MINI male on the other end. You would call this adapter an RCA-FEMALE-TO-MINI-MALE ADAPTER. Figure 2-16 shows an assortment of adapters. Study them to get a feel for the nomenclature.

ADAPTERS solve a lot of hookup problems, but they also cause problems. They are a weak link in your audio system, sometimes wiggling loose and making poor contact, which results in no audio or a crackling sound. If you lose your sound, check your adapters by wiggling them; if the problem becomes chronic, remove the old plug and install a new plug of the right type.

HIGH- AND LOW-LEVEL SIGNALS

Microphones make weak LO-LEVEL signals. Mixers, public-address systems, tuners, VCRs, audiocassette players, and other devices that use electric power make stronger HI-LEVEL signals. LO-LEVEL signals are meant to go to a tape recorder's microphone input (MIC IN). HI-LEVEL signals are meant to go to a recorder's HI-LEVEL inputs (AUDIO IN or AUX IN or LINE IN). When recording music or other sounds from these high-powered devices, you don't want to send this audio signal to the supersensitive MIC IN on your VCR, camcorder, or audiocassette deck: your sound will probably come out distorted and raspy. Conversely, you don't want to send a microphone signal to the AUX or AUDIO IN of a VCR or a mixer; your sound will be thin, weak, or inaudible. You can tell a signal is HI-LEVEL if the output is labeled LINE OUT, HI-LEVEL OUT, PREAMP OUT, PHONE, PROGRAM OUT, AUDIO OUT, EAR, or MONITOR OUT.

Some machines have only one audio input, the MIC IN. In these cases, to use music from a tape player, mixer, or tuner, you need to weaken the signal before sending it to the MIC IN. The device to do this is called a PAD or ATTENUATOR. It costs about $3, is the size of your little finger, and connects between your audio cable and your recorder's MIC IN. This gadget "throws away" most of the sound signal, bringing it down to a volume that the machine can handle.

Some audio devices have earphone, headphone, or speaker outputs, some of whose signal outputs are too strong even for the AUX, LINE, or AUDIO IN of a recorder or a mixer. Again, the recorded sound will come out raspy and distorted; again, the solution is to run your signal through an ATTENUATOR to weaken it. Figure 2-17 reviews some of these inputs, outputs, and whatputs.

Do not confuse IMPEDANCE with LEVEL. The two have nothing to do with each other. If something happens to be HI-Z *and* HI-LEVEL, it's only coincidental.

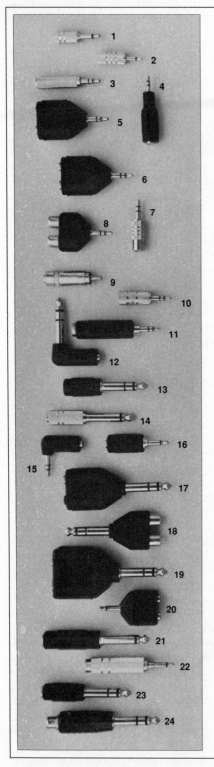

1 Accepts 3/32" subminiature stereo plug. Plugs into 1/8" mono jack. Use with lightweight stereo headsets with monaural CB scanners, recorders, radios.

2 Accepts 1/8" stereo plug. Plugs into 3/32" mono jack.

3 Accepts 3/32" stereo plug. Plugs into 1/8" stereo jack. Use stereo headphones having a 3/32" (submini) plug with stereo portables having 1/8" jack.

4 Accepts 1/8" stereo plug. Plugs into 3/32" stereo jack.

5 Accepts two 1/8" mono plugs. Plugs into 1/8" stereo jack. Use to dub from personal portable stereo to a home deck. Outputs are L/R coded.

6 Accepts two 1/8" stereo plugs. Plugs into 1/8" stereo jack. Y-adapter lets you use two stereo headsets with one personal stereo.

7 Accepts phono plug. Plugs into 1/8" stereo jack.

8 Accepts two phono plugs. Plugs into 1/8" stereo jack.

9 Accepts 1/8" stereo plug. Plugs into phono jack.

10 Accepts 1/8" mono plug. Plugs into 1/8" stereo jack. Use to dub from mono portable to a stereo recorder. Combines L/R channels.

11 Accepts 1/4" stereo plug. Plugs into 1/8" stereo jack.

12 Accepts 1/8" stereo plug. Plugs into 1/4" stereo jack. Right-angle type. Use mini stereo headphones with equipment having 1/4" stereo jacks.

13 Straight version of number 12.

14 Accepts 1/8" stereo plug. Plugs into 1/4" mono jack. Use comfortable mini stereo headphones with ham, shortwave, CB, and scanner radios.

15 Accepts 1/8" stereo or mono plug. Plugs into 1/8" stereo or mono jack. 90° bend helps prevent cord and jack damage.

16 Accepts 1/8" stereo plug. Plugs into 1/8" mono jack. Use stereo headphones with TVs, radios, recorders, walkie-talkies, and scanners.

17 Accepts two 1/4" mono plugs. Plugs into 1/4" stereo jack.

18 Accepts two phono plugs. Plugs into 1/4" stereo jack. Excellent for use with dub-out jack on stereo receivers. Outputs are L/R coded.

19 Accepts two 1/4" stereo plugs. Plugs into 1/4" stereo jack.

20 Accepts two 1/8" mono plugs. Plugs into 1/8" mono jack.

21 Accepts 1/4" stereo plug. Plugs into 1/4" mono jack. Use stereo headphones with mono CB, ham, shortwave, and scanner radios.

22 Accepts 1/8" stereo plug. Plugs into 1/8" mono jack.

23 Accepts 1/8" mono plug. Plugs into 1/4" stereo jack.

24 Accepts phono plug. Plugs into 1/4" stereo jack. Provides mono output from stereo receiver dub-out or headphone jack.

FIGURE 2-16 Audio adapters

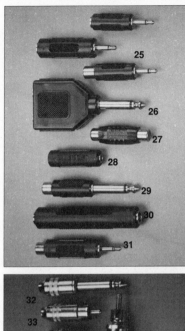

25 Three-piece mono adapter set. Adapts 3/32" submini plug, 1/4" phone plug, or phono plug to plug into 1/8" mono jack.

26 Accepts two 1/4" mono phone plugs. Plugs into 1/4" mono jack. Use two mikes with single mike input on recorder or amplifier.

27 Accepts two phono plugs. Use to connect two cables with phono plugs.

28 Accepts two 1/8" stereo or mono plugs. Coupler.

29 Accepts phono plug. Plugs into 1/4" mono jack.

30 Accepts two 1/4" stereo or mono phone plugs. Coupler.

31 Signal reducer. Accepts phono plug. Plugs into 1/8" mono jack. Built-in 40-dB attenuator lets you use a portable recorder's mike input to tape from line-level, aux, or tape-out sources without distortion.

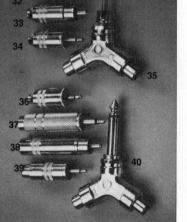

32 Accepts 1/8" plug. Plugs into 1/4" jack.

33 Accepts 1/8" plug. Plugs into phono jack.

34 Accepts 3/32" submini plug. Plugs into 1/8" jack.

35 Accepts two phono plugs. Plugs into phono jack. Y-adapter for combining or dividing mono signals.

36 Accepts 1/8" plug. Plugs into 3/32" submini jack.

37 Accepts 1/4" phone plug. Plugs into 1/8" jack.

38 Accepts 1/4" phone plug. Plugs into phono jack.

39 Accepts phono plug. Plugs into 1/8" jack.

40 Accepts two phono plugs. Plugs into 1/4" phone jack. Y-adapter for combining or dividing signals.

41 Adapter/transformer. Accepts 1/4" phone plug. Plugs into XLR jack. Lets you use a HI-Z unbalanced mike with equipment that requires LO-Z balanced input. Use with number 42 to minimize high-frequency loss in long cable runs.

42 Adapter/transformer. Accepts XLR plug. Plugs into 1/4" phone jack. Use a mike having a "pro" plug with amplifier or recorder that has 1/4" jack. Adapts LO-Z to HI-Z unbalanced input.

43 XLR in-line socket. Mates with numbers 44 and 41. Cable strain relief.

44 Three-pin XLR plug. All-metal die-cast body for durability and shielding.

45 XLR panel socket. Latching type with push release. Accepts numbers 44 and 41.

FIGURE 2-16 Audio adapters (continued)

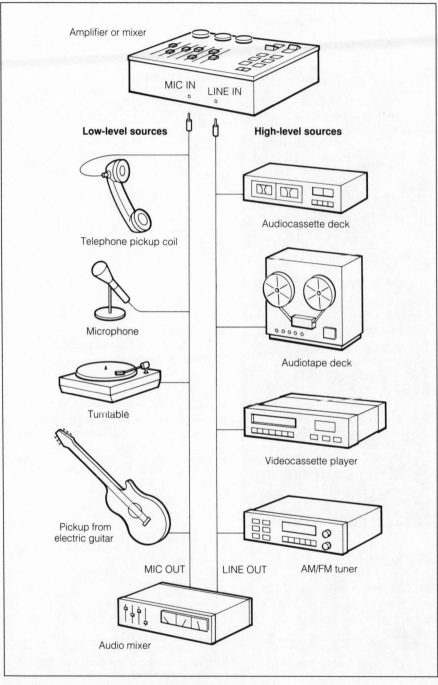

Amplifier or mixer

MIC IN LINE IN

Low-level sources **High-level sources**

Telephone pickup coil

Audiocassette deck

Microphone

Audiotape deck

Turntable

Videocassette player

Pickup from
electric guitar

MIC OUT LINE OUT AM/FM tuner

Audio mixer

FIGURE 2-17 High-level and low-level audio sources

MICROPHONE STANDS AND MOUNTS

Shock Mounts

If you hold a mike in your hand, you'll probably pick up the creaking and crackling of your mike cord, the thumping of your fingers, or the wind as you move the mike around. If you *must* hold your mike, consider using one with a SHOCK MOUNT, a special cushion that places insulation between the microphone's sound-sensitive insides and the shell of the mike, absorbing hand and cable noises.

For slight cable noises, try tying a loose overhand knot in the mike cable 3 inches from the microphone. This can act as a *stress relief* and absorb the little tugs on the mike. Another trick is to run the cord from a LAV mike inside a person's shirt and pant leg so that the tugging occurs at the ankle rather than at the mike.

SHOTGUN microphones, because they pick up more creaking and rumbling from hand motion than other mikes, desperately require a separate SHOCK MOUNT when held. (Review Figure 2-9.)

Desk Stands and Floor Stands

With a DESK or FLOOR stand you can raise or lower the mike for proper positioning. Standup speakers or singers often use FLOOR stands. On the top of the adjustable pole is a screw-on mike holder that allows the mike to be removed, carried about, and then clipped back into its holder. The FLOOR stand, the base of which is heavy enough to keep the mike from tipping over, distances the microphone from the sound of scuffling feet. If you still pick up floor vibrations, consider placing the mike stand on something spongy like a carpet remnant, or two or three layers of pizza pie with pepperoni.

If the mike stand is going to appear on camera, avoid shiny chrome because the bright reflections of lights or the sun will bedazzle your TV camera and may even damage older-model cameras. Instead, opt for charcoal gray or brown.

Boom Mike Stands

A BOOM is the sound that you hear when a microphone stand falls over. It is also the name of the long arm that holds the microphone out in front of the performer. The simplest BOOM is the FISHPOLE—just a stick with a microphone on the end that allows you to follow someone moving around while keeping the microphone out of a TV camera's picture.

Another popular BOOM is the BABY BOOM in Figure 2-18. (If it had been invented just after World War II, it could have been named the "Postwar Baby Boom.") It keeps your stand out of the way so that the audience or cameras can see the performer better. It also can reach down near the bottoms of violas, saxophones, drums, and basses.

The BABY BOOM attaches to the top of a DESK or FLOOR stand and adjusts to aim in different directions. A counterweight at the end of the pole helps balance the weight of the microphone. Be sure to loosen the tighteners on the BABY BOOM before adjusting it to avoid stripping the grooved tightening mechanism.

FIGURE 2-18 Baby boom

COPING WITH CABLES

As you accumulate audio machinery, the jungle of wires will grow, complete with exotic birds and drumbeats. There are several ways to make a path through the cable jungle. One way is with a machete, quick but expensive. A slower but more civilized way is to *label* the cables with a masking tape tag telling where each goes to (or comes from). Then coil up any excess wire and strap the loops together. Unravel any kinks or knots. Professionals use CABLE TIES, little plastic strips that can be pulled tightly around cables to strap them together.

The most terrifying sound in the recording jungle is "oops—crash." It's the unwelcome sound of a shoe snagging a cable and bringing a mike stand with its expensive microphone to the floor. Whenever possible, slip your cables under a carpet or tape them to the floor using wide duct tape. Run them *over* doorways, if possible.

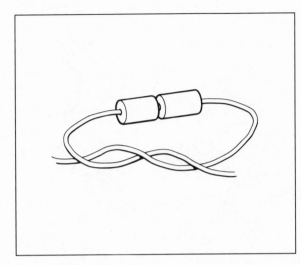

FIGURE 2-19
Overhand knot to keep plugs
from becoming unfastened

To keep mike extension cords from becoming unfastened, tie them in an overhand knot as shown in Figure 2-19. (This technique is good for disconnect-proofing electric extension cords too.)

One sure way to damage a wire is to disconnect the plug by pulling on the wire itself. Instead, *always* grasp the plug by the plug body to avoid strain on the wire in the weak place where the cable enters the plug.

MICROPHONE SELECTION
AND PLACEMENT

Just getting sound is pretty easy; home video camcorders and many portable audiocassette decks have miniature electret condenser microphones built into them. These mikes record speech very well, especially if you can get the machine close enough to the person so that you are not picking up excessive room echoes. This is not professional sound, but it will get by. If you are using a separate microphone, almost any mike will do assuming the plug fits. Presumably, however, you bought this book because you wanted to do better than "good enough," so this chapter will focus on setting up the best microphone in exactly the right spot for each situation.

GENERAL RULES

For the best sound, use LO-Z mikes with BALANCED LINES that will introduce the least interference and noise into your signal. Generally, the closer the microphone to the subject, the clearer and less echoey the sound. If you are recording several people or instruments, a close microphone allows one mike to pick up one instrument's sound while another mike picks up another instrument. You can record these sounds separately and blend them later. More-distant microphones will pick up both instruments at once, and you won't be able to raise the volume of one without raising the volume of the other.

Placing a microphone *too close* to the performer (say 3 inches) often results in the mike picking up unsavory snorts and lip noises. Directional mikes pick up too much bass; when your performer pronounces "Peter Piper picked a peck of pickled peppers," the p's will sound like cannon fire.

PHASE

When you hear sound, vibrating air molecules are first pushing on your eardrum and then pulling on it. If two sounds were IN-PHASE, then their vibrations would be pushing the molecules twice as hard in one direction and twice as hard in the other direction, effectively doubling the power of the sound. If two tones were OUT-OF-PHASE, the opposite would happen. The first sound would be making air molecules push on your eardrum while the second sound would be trying to make air molecules pull on your eardrum. The sounds would be fighting each other, *decreasing* the power of the sound. The resulting sound may be weak, hollow, spacy, whooshy, thin, or outright inaudible.

In audio, we always want sounds to be IN-PHASE. That means that if you have two speakers, they should be wired so that the speaker diaphragms are both coming toward you at the same time and going away from you at the same time, compressing and rarifying the air as a team, making sound that is IN-PHASE, strengthening itself. The same is true for microphones. If you place a microphone in front of a wall, for instance, one sound could go straight into the mike while the other, bouncing off the wall and reaching the mike OUT-OF-PHASE with the first sound, weakens it. If you are using two microphones spaced some distance apart, one mike could pick up a sound before the other does (it takes some time for the sound to travel to the second mike), thus the second mike may be picking up OUT-OF-PHASE sound. If you combine these two signals in a microphone mixer, the total sound could be *weaker* rather than *stronger*. If you tape-record the two sounds on separate tracks and then mix the two tracks together, again the OUT-OF-PHASE sound will weaken the total effect.

One exasperating aspect of this phase business is that one frequency may be OUT-OF-PHASE for a pair of microphones (or a mike and a reflector) and another frequency be IN-PHASE. Thus, if you are recording music the IN-PHASE tones will be strong and the OUT-OF-PHASE tones will be weak, creating a strange and hollow effect.

Place mike on a thin cushion to insulate against table noises. Ninety-nine percent of the bounced sound is in-phase because the bounce is so short. Sound is actually strengthened.

Voice

FIGURE 3-1 Performer speaks into one microphone on a table to obtain in-phase sound reflections

Applying these theories to the real world, we learn to place omnidirectional mikes *away* from walls, desks, and other hard surfaces that could reflect OUT-OF-PHASE sound waves. If using directional microphones, the problem is not so great because the mike will listen primarily in the direction it is pointed, rejecting some of these OUT-OF-PHASE echoes.

This PHASE business can also work for you. Placing a microphone on a table, as shown in Figure 3-1, allows the mike to capture the direct sounds and the reflected sounds at exactly the same moment, making them IN-PHASE and strengthening them. This is also how a pressure-zone microphone (PZM) works. By using a phenomenon called the BOUNDARY EFFECT, the PZM gathers up IN-PHASE waves to make a strong signal.

Figure 3-2 shows another way to use the BOUNDARY EFFECT. By placing the head of the microphone at the edge of the script or next to some other flat surface, the direct sounds and the reflected sounds both hit the mike IN-PHASE.

We will come back to this PHASE business later in the chapter when we talk about stereo. Before diving into more heavy metal, let's now cover some simple mike setups.

Place mike at edge of script stand and slightly in front of it. Ninety percent of sound is in-phase from the short bounce. This setup makes the script easy to read and reduces the performer's head bobbing up and down, which affects the sound.

Voice

FIGURE 3-2 Placement of script for in-phase sound reflections

ONE PERSON, ONE MICROPHONE

Hand and Stand Mikes

If the performer is sitting at a desk or standing at a podium, a CARDIOID or UNIDIREC-TIONAL mike on a floor or desk stand may be best. If the mike can be placed very close to the person, an OMNIDIRECTIONAL mike will also work. The farther away the mike is from the performer, the more room echoes and the more you'll need a DIRECTIONAL microphone to reject them. CARDIOIDS work well because they allow the talent (performer) some freedom of movement without affecting the sound.

The larger handheld and stand microphones have excellent FREQUENCY RESPONSE and can handle a wide range of volume, making them excellent for singers or instrumentalists. One added advantage of a mike on a stand is that it is so far from a large surface (the floor) that sound reflections are insignificant. Carpeted floors are even less reflective.

Lavalier, Lapel, and Tie Clip Mikes

If the talent is sitting, standing, or walking around, a LAVALIER, LAPEL CLIP, or TIE CLIP mike may be best. They don't give terrific music fidelity but are excellent for speech. Being close to the talent's mouth, they reject room noise and provide excellent "presence" (intimacy).

Position the LAVALIER or LAPEL mike about 6 inches from the performer's mouth. If the performer is on TV and will be looking left most of the time, perhaps toward the host, then place the LAPEL mike on the guest's *left* lapel so that he is turned toward the mike most of the time.

If the performer expects to move around a lot, attach the mike wire to his body or have him hold some wire in his hand so that it will trail along easily and not tug on the mike. The wire could be threaded under a jacket or down a pant leg.

If the mike mustn't show, hide it under a thin layer of clothing. Silk, chiffon, polyester, and other synthetics create static electricity, which can add pops and clicks to your sound. Either spray these fabrics with an antistatic laundry spray or have your performers wear cottons and wools. If possible, have the mike peek out through a buttonhole or other opening.

If your performer twists a lot, causing the mike cable to creak and thump, try tying a loose overhand knot in the cable about 3 inches from the base of the mike to absorb some of the cable movement.

A popular place to hide a LAPEL mike is in a woman's cleavage, but this can be a problem; the sound reflections there can give it a flat or hollow sound.

Boom Mikes

If you are shooting video with an active performer, you can stick your mike on the end of a pole and try to keep it out of the picture. You can either hold the mike above the performer's head or down near his knees pointing up at the face. Remember that the mike near the floor will pick up the scuffling of feet while the one overhead may cast a shadow.

Shotgun Mikes

Because BOOM mikes can intrude on the picture, most videographers like to use SHOTGUN mikes, which can be held farther from the talent. If the performer stays in one spot, mount the SHOTGUN on a stand just like a regular mike. If the performer dances around, then you'll need to have someone aim the mike, following the performer as he moves. Anyone charged with this task should wear headphones and listen to the signal from the mike. This will improve the sound person's attentiveness to accurate aiming. SHOTGUNS are susceptible to wind and motion noises; use a WIND-SCREEN and SHOCK MOUNT whenever necessary.

FM Wireless Mikes

If your performer is being fired out of a cannon, is an undercover agent documenting a heavy crack deal, or is an acrobatic singer gyrating on stage, then a microphone cable may be a problem (see Figure 3-3). The solution may be an FM or WIRELESS microphone. Instead of sending its signal down a wire to your mixer or recorder, it sends a radio wave to an FM receiver that sends *its* signal down a wire to your mixer or recorder.

The better WIRELESS mikes transmit farther and with clearer sound, but in any case keep as close to the subject as possible and keep metal obstructions away from your receiver's antenna.

Inexpensive FM mikes can be tuned to various frequencies on your FM radio (or even a portable FM radio that can attach to your portable camcorder). Tune the transmitter to a vacant channel in your area so that its signal doesn't get interference from a radio station on the same frequency. These amateur WIRELESS mikes pick up a lot of hiss and crackling, and the signal fades in and out as you move around. The better models cost $70 and up and use a dedicated FM receiver tuned to the mike's frequency. The more expensive models ($1,000+) have special noise-limiting circuits and double antennas to ensure a clean signal.

TWO PEOPLE, ONE MICROPHONE

Ideally, each person should have a separate mike so you can adjust the volume of each source independently. If this isn't possible, try to get one mike to hear two people and the least room noise. The two people can shift the mike back and forth, as in a news interview. If two people are sitting close together, a CARDIOID mike will pick them up pretty well from 2 feet away. Aim it half way between them or more toward the softer-spoken person.

A LAVALIER mike won't pick up two people at once; the person not wearing the LAV will be almost inaudible.

SEVERAL PEOPLE, SEVERAL MIKES

A mike for each speaker is still the best situation, but you can run out of mikes or mixer inputs. As a compromise, try grouping people into threes and aiming a CARDIOID toward each group. Another option is to plant an OMNI in the middle of the group with a LAV or CARDIOID dedicated to the group leader.

FIGURE 3-3 Cable problems you can avoid by using FM microphones

PZM mikes are handy for groups; they pick up everyone speaking around a table and do a good job of rejecting room echo. Just place the PZM mike in the middle of the table. Beware of paper rustling, pencils rolling, fingers drumming, and knees knocking against the table.

For meetings where the speakers will use a podium and the audience will be asking questions, place one mike at the podium and another on a stand in the aisle for the audience (audience members step up to the mike in the aisle when asking their questions). Use a DIRECTIONAL mike in the aisle to reject FEEDBACK from the loudspeakers. No, FEEDBACK is not the chef's position on a football team. It is the loud screech or whoop that you hear when sound goes in a mike, gets amplified, comes out the loudspeakers, and, in a vicious circle, returns to the mike.

News conferences can be miked with a SHOTGUN and an alert assistant who aims the microphone toward each person speaking.

MUSICAL RECORDINGS

High fidelity is your goal. LAVALIER mikes are designed for speech, not for music. The best fidelity usually comes from HANDHELD or STAND mikes. When possible, mike each performer separately or group the performers.

With a HYPERCARDIOID mike, you can record a whole choir with a single mike placed the same distance away from the group as the group is wide (see Figure 3-4). CARDIOID mikes need to be a little closer. Or try a PZM on the floor in front of the group as far away from the frontmost member as that person is tall.

Another PZM technique is to hang the PZM in front of the singers. Attach the mike to a square-foot sheet of Masonite or Plexiglas to improve sensitivity and bass response.

When miking bands and orchestras, try to separate the instruments into groups so they can share microphones. This gives you independent volume control for each section of the band. You could, for instance, arc groups of instruments around a CARDIOID and place an OMNI in the drum cluster to pick up the drums. For pianos, open the lid and place the mike several yards away or place the mike several feet from the high strings diagonally aimed at the low strings.

When miking electric guitar players, you can place the mike in front of the guitar speaker or connect your mixer to the amplifier's AUX OUT. Violins, mandolins, banjos, guitars, cellos, and basses deflect their sound forward. Place your mike 2 feet in front of these instruments and aim it toward them. Horns, drums, and electric guitar speakers also shoot the sounds straight out but louder; place the mike 3 feet away or more, aiming at the source. Woodwinds and flutes create airy breathing noises near their mouthpieces. Mike them from behind the performer, aiming the mike over the talent's shoulder.

Some rock bands play so loud that the mike distorts the sound. Unless you have a professional mike designed for this abuse, you may have to place your microphone up to 25 feet away.

RECORDING STEREO

Record stereo using either a stereo mike or two separate microphones. The sound from one mike goes to one CHANNEL of your stereo recorder; the other mike sends its signal to the other CHANNEL.

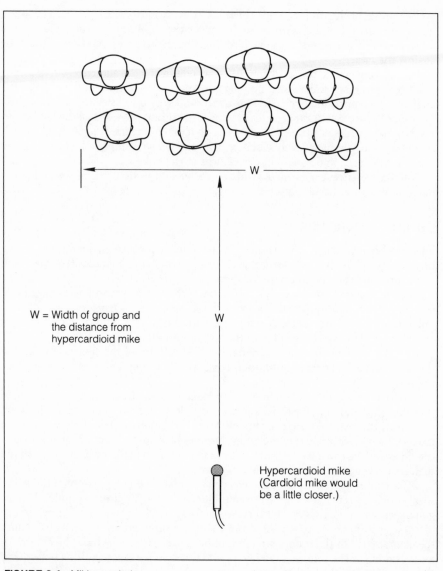

FIGURE 3-4 Miking a choir

Sometimes separating the mikes so they each hear something different improves the stereo effect. Doing this, however, runs the risk of OUT-OF-PHASE problems when the sound goes in one mike before the other. Monitoring the sound with stereo headphones doesn't reveal the problem—your ears hardly hear the OUT-OF-PHASE sound—but if your tape is played on a monaural machine, the signals will cancel each other, giving you a hollow, echoey, or tinny effect.

One way to set up two mikes for stereo recording is to place the heads of two CARDIOID or DIRECTIONAL mikes together at a 90-degree angle so that one mike picks up mostly the left field and the other, the right (see Figure 3-5).

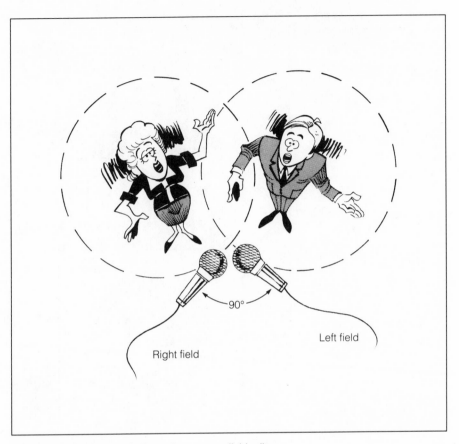

FIGURE 3-5   Stereo recording using two cardioid mikes

The easiest solution is to use a STEREOPHONIC microphone, which listens in two directions at once. Some of these can be adjusted to give more or less of a stereo effect.

STEREO is not meant to be one instrument playing into the left ear and another instrument playing into the right ear. Truly realistic sound reproduction creates an imaginary CENTER CHANNEL that gives the impression that things are happening in the middle *between* the distant left and right channels. To make your recordings sound more natural, allow some of the left sound to go into the right CHANNEL and some of the right sound to go into the left CHANNEL.

Now let's apply this to microphones. If you are using a pair of CARDIOIDS as in Figure 3-5, increase the angle between the two mikes to increase the stereo effect. Conversely, if you decrease the angle between the two mikes, their areas of sensitivity will overlap, creating a larger CENTER CHANNEL and less of a stereo effect. The trick is to select an angle that creates the most pleasing natural sound. This is as much an art as it is a science.

Incidentally, using OMNI mikes won't work because both mikes hear the performers on the left and right equally. Using HYPERCARDIOID or SHOTGUN mikes won't work either because they listen to a very small defined area, creating too strong a stereo effect.

FIGURE 3-6
Wrong way to use two mikes

REDUNDANT MIKES

If your microphone fails during a graduation speech in front of a thousand people, guess whose career goes down the tubes? For important occasions, set up two mikes; if one fails, the other is working.

There is a wrong and a right way to place two mikes on a podium. Figure 3-6 shows the wrong way. Can you see why? Figure 3-7 shows the right setup. Notice the difference. In Figure 3-7 the heads of the two mikes are very close together, making it nearly impossible for the sound to get OUT OF PHASE as the person moves around. If you use two CARDIOID mikes, their pickup areas will overlap and cover the entire front of the podium or desk area. This mike setup is the same as for stereo recording (see Figure 3-5).

TIE CLIP mikes can be made redundant by clipping two mikes, one above the other, to the performer's tie or lapel. There are also double clips that will hold two TIE CLIP mikes at once.

FIGURE 3-7
Right way to use two mikes

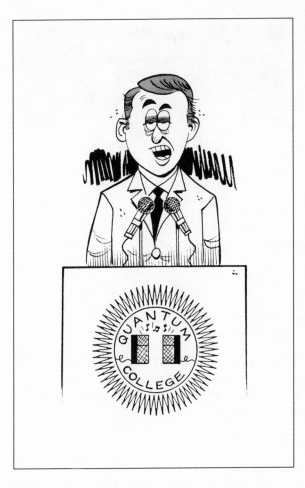

FIGURE 3-7
Right way to use two mikes

BANISHING UNWANTED NOISE FROM THE RECORDING

Getting audible sound is one thing. Getting it without background noise and echoes is everything.

Wind Noise

Even a slight breeze over a microphone can cause a deep rumbling and rattling that sounds like a thunderstorm in the background of your recording. Some solutions:

1. Stay out of the wind and don't interview politicians.
2. Buy a WINDSCREEN (see Figure 3-8) that fits over the mike and protects it from breezes while letting other sounds through.
3. In a pinch, put your sock over the mike to deflect the wind. Be prepared for wisecracks like "your audio stinks."

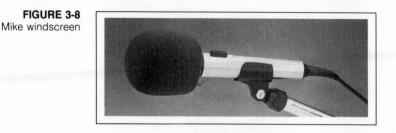

FIGURE 3-8
Mike windscreen

Hand Noise

The shuffling and crackling of nervous hands holding a microphone can ruin your recording. Set the mike on a stand or hang a LAVALIER around the talent's neck warning, "don't touch it, don't touch it, don't touch it!" If the performer *must* handle the mike, tell him to merely grip it and not to fidget with it or fondle it or play with the cord.

Stand Noise

A mike on a table stand sounds like a kettle drum rolling down a stairwell every time the talent bumps the table. Some solutions:

1. Have the talent keep his or her hands and knees still (or hogtie the performer to his chair).
2. Insulate the base of the mike stand from the table with a piece of carpet, a typewriter pad, a quiche lorraine, or anything spongy.

Lavalier Noise

Too tight a cord results in excessive throat sounds (a cord that is really tight results in the sound of gagging and gasping for air). A very loose cord can cause the mike to swing like a pendulum and bump things like buttons. Before recording anything with a LAVALIER, check that there are no buttons or tie clasps for the mike to clank against.

Mouth Noise

Performers love to put their lips to the mike, perhaps because they don't trust the wizardry of electronics to sense their feeble sounds from a foot away and amplify them to spellbinding proportions. Then whenever the performer is loud, the sound distorts. When the performer pronounces the letters *t*, *b*, and especially *p*, it sounds like bombs bursting in air. Some solutions:

1. Teach performers to trust the mike and keep their distance. (Cover the top of the mike with erect porcupine quills.)
2. Use professional proximity mikes that have wire screens to put some distance between the lips and the actual microphone and contain "pop" filters.

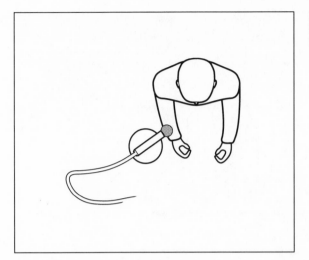

FIGURE 3-9
Mike's angle avoids
popping *p*'s

3. Angle the mike as shown in Figure 3-9 so that the offensive *p*'s and *b*'s fly forward, hurting no one. The mike will still pick up the performer's voice. Incidentally, these noises are less noticeable when using an OMNI mike: the more DIRECTIONAL the mike, the more noticeable the problem.

Room Noise

Keep the mike close to the talent. Use CARDIOID and DIRECTIONAL mikes to reject extraneous room noise. Place your performer away from windows, fans, and loudspeakers; use rooms with plenty of carpeting, curtains, and soft furniture. Don't be afraid to hang blankets on the walls.

Feedback

FEEDBACK is the sound of your microphone coming out of a loudspeaker and going back into your mike. 'Round and 'round it goes, getting louder all the time. Some solutions:

1. Monitor your sound with headphones so that the mike doesn't hear the sound.

2. Keep the loudspeaker volumes low so that they don't feed back into the mike.

3. Place your mike and loudspeakers so that the sound from the loudspeakers doesn't get into your mike. The best speaker position is probably to the side of the mike and as far away from the mike as possible. Figures 3-10 and 3-11 show improper and proper ways to set up a mike and loudspeaker system.

4. Use a DIRECTIONAL mike positioned so that it hears the performer but doesn't hear the loudspeakers.

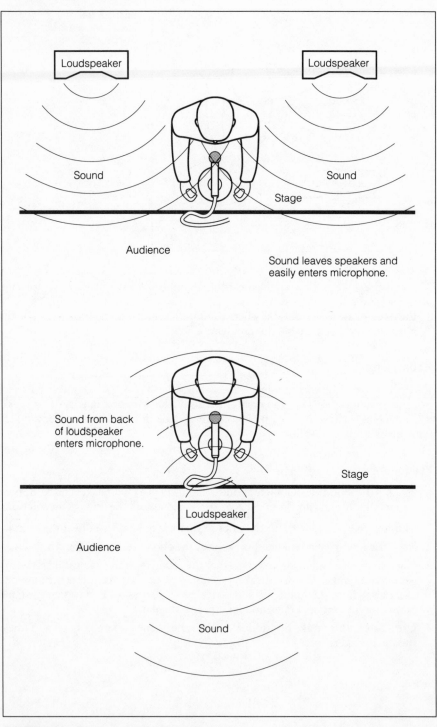

FIGURE 3-10 Situations that cause feedback

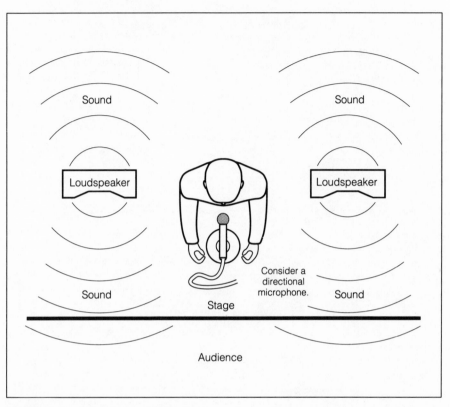

FIGURE 3-11 Setup that avoids feedback

MIXERS

A MIXER is an audio device that mixes audio signals together (catchy name, no?). Each signal can be adjusted for loudness (all the way down to no loudness at all), and the combination of these audio signals can be sent to an audio recorder, VCR, or loudspeaker system. Figure 4-1 shows some basic, moderate, and miraculous mixers. Stereo mixers allow the sound from each source to be fed to the left channel, the right channel, or both channels equally. A knob called the PAN POT makes this adjustment.

MIXER INPUTS

Microphones are generally plugged into the MIC INPUT sockets in the back of the mixer, up to one mike for each volume control knob. The more professional models have XLR inputs for BALANCED LINES.

For HIGH-LEVEL signals like those from FM tuners, VCRs, or other tape machines, the MIXER generally has less-sensitive AUX, LINE IN, or HI-LEVEL inputs to mix prerecorded musical background or sound effects with voices from the microphones.

Professional mixers have switches next to each input labeled HI-Z/LO-Z. These switches change the IMPEDANCE of the input; when in doubt, throw the switch both ways and choose the one that sounds the best.

When you've plugged in and tested all your mikes, label the knobs on the mixer with masking tape so that you know which knob is which. This saves bumbling and fumbling during the recording session.

Pads

Some mixers, instead of having separate HI-LEVEL and LO-LEVEL inputs, use the same input to do two jobs. A button labeled PAD or –20 dB is pressed to make the input less sensitive, appropriate for HI-LEVEL signals. If some day you plug in a mike and get almost no signal from it, check your mixer's PAD switch to see if it is in the wrong position.

Other mixers have knob-type controls to adjust the INPUT SENSITIVITY of your mixer. Here's how you use it:

1. Turn the INPUT SENSITIVITY knob up halfway.

2. Turn the individual volume control or slider up three-fourths of the way.

3. Turn the MASTER volume control up three-fourths of the way.

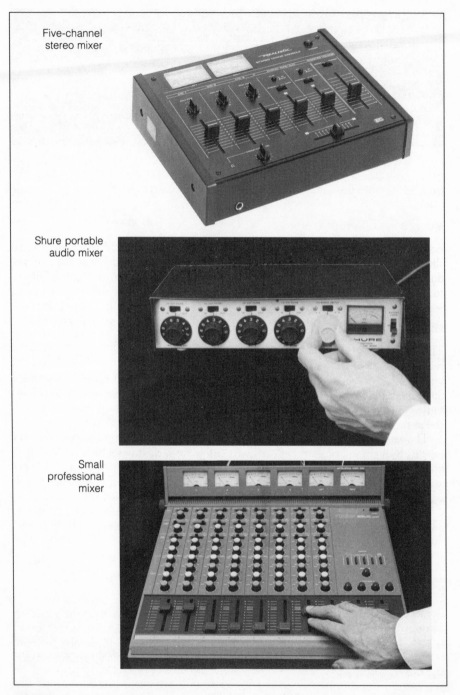

Five-channel
stereo mixer

Shure portable
audio mixer

Small
professional
mixer

FIGURE 4-1 Audio mixers

4. Send a test signal through the mixer. If the volume is way too loud or the little PEAK lights near the INPUT SENSITIVITY knobs flash on, then the knob is set too high. Turn it down. If your sound is very weak, turn the knob up. Once this knob is set, make the rest of your volume adjustments with the individual and MASTER controls.

Phono

Some mixers have special inputs for phonograph turntables with special EQUALIZATION circuits built into them to improve the sound from CERAMIC or MAGNETIC phonograph cartridges. There may also be a switch to accommodate the special tone of these two kinds of cartridges. If you tried to send the signal from a turntable directly into the MIC inputs of a mixer, your treble would be too strong and your bass too weak. The frequencies from the turntable must be EQUALIZED to come out right.

Multiple Input Control

Some mixers allow you to plug ten sources into the back but only have five knobs or sliders (called POTENTIOMETERS or POTS) on the front. This saves space assuming you don't use all ten sources at once. A switch on the mixer allows one control to "listen" to one source or another.

MIXER OUTPUTS

The mixer's output sends the combined signals to your amplifier, VCR, or audio recorder. Just as each microphone's volume is adjustable with a knob on the mixer, the volume of the mixer's signal is adjusted by the MASTER volume control—usually a different color or shape than the others. Turning the MASTER down turns down all the signals at once, which is convenient if you wish to fade down six volume controls at the same time and you aren't an octopus.

The mixer may have one or several outputs for feeding amplifiers, monitors, and tape decks. These outputs could be HI-LEVEL for feeding the AUX IN of a recorder or amplifier or LO-LEVEL OUT for feeding the microphone inputs of amplifiers or recorders.

Headphone

This output monitors the audio signal over headphones and may even have its own volume control, which does not affect the sound going through the mixer. It is there only for your listening comfort.

Effects Out

Sometimes you want to send your whole signal or parts of your signal to an echo chamber, graphic equalizer, or some other audio-processing device. The EFFECTS OUT or ECHO SEND output lets you select *parts* of your audio signal and route them to a special output. Once the outboard device has massaged the sound, it sends the result back into the mixer, perhaps to an ECHO RECEIVE or EFFECTS RECEIVE or AUX RECEIVE input. Now you can mix the modified sound with the other sounds going into the mixer and send the final result to your recorder or amplifier.

Cue or Audition or Monitor

This output, found on more-professional mixers, allows you to preview a sound before it is recorded or made public. By pressing a CUE switch or turning a CUE volume control for that source, you can send its signal to your headphones or to a special amplifier/ speaker for only *you* to hear. Once you are happy with the sound, turn up the regular volume control to let the sound mix with the others or be recorded.

OTHER MIXER GADGETS

As mixers go up in price, you get more bells and whistles than you could ever ring or blow.

Filters

A FILTER, as the name implies, removes something from the sound signal. A LO-CUT FILTER is a switch on some of the smaller mixers that reduces low frequencies such as wind rumble or removes the RUMBLE of cheap phonograph turntables.

Switch the LO-CUT FILTER IN (or ON) to remove the bassy sounds in a person's voice making it easier to listen to. You would switch the FILTER OUT (OFF) when you wanted to record music with full fidelity.

Parametric Equalizer

Large mixers contain PARAMETRIC EQUALIZERS—adjustable audio filters that can be tuned to boost or cut a selected frequency and then adjusted to control how vigorously that frequency is removed or boosted. By tuning a PARAMETRIC EQUALIZER to 60 Hz, for instance, and then turning the BOOST/CUT adjustment all the way *down*, you will remove 60-cycle hum from your recording along with some other deep bassy sounds. Turning the knob in the other direction will *boost* the bass. If you want normal fidelity, turn the knob to FLAT, which means the mixer is equally sensitive to all frequencies.

ADJUSTING AUDIO LEVELS

Many VCRs and audiocassette recorders have AUTOMATIC VOLUME CONTROLS (AVC) or AUTOMATIC GAIN CONTROLS (AGC) that electronically sense the sound going into the device and automatically adjust the volume to a proper level.

The more professional equipment allows you to *choose* that volume. To help you decide on the proper level of sound, these mixers, VCRs, audiocassette recorders, and amplifiers have meters—or light-emitting diodes (LEDs) set up as meters—to appraise you of your volume level. Cheap, nonprofessional meters are generally tiny, with a little needle inside and a scale with a red area. The volume should be high enough to make the needle wiggle but not go into the red area. The better equipment has what is called a VU meter. The VU stands for VOLUME UNIT, which is a measure of sound loudness. The same meter may be marked off in decibels (dB) or percent. The meter guides you to the perfect volume. Every audio device is designed to handle a certain signal strength, a perfect volume of sound. Anything less than that is too weak a signal that uses less than the full capacity of the equipment. Weak recordings are likely to play back with hum and hiss in the background. Anything more than the perfect volume presents too strong a signal that saturates the circuits or tape and

FIGURE 4-2
Mixer's meter at 0 VU

eventually causes distortion in the sound. Your game plan is to make the circuits work as hard as they can but not too hard.

The perfect audio level is 0 VU, 0 dB, or 100% on the meter's scale as shown in Figure 4-2. As people speak or music plays, the meter should wiggle between 0 and 100% (−20 and 0 on the VU or dB scale). Try to keep the meter as close to the 100% mark as possible. Occasionally the needle will overshoot, dipping into the red up to +1, +2, or +3 VU. This is okay. Although the signal is too loud, it will probably be gone in a second and not hurt anything. If the needle hangs in the red too much, though, a louder sound may send the needle right off the scale.

When the needle jumps off the scale, the sound distorts and becomes raspy, something like what you hear on the beach when a surfer turns his portable radio volume up all the way. If you let the meter go off the scale while making a recording, you will saturate the tape with magnetism. If you record the tape with distortion, every time you play it back you will hear the distortion, even if you play it softly. The only way to get rid of the noise is to record the tape again properly.

The specifications on audio equipment often tell you how many dB you can overdrive it before it distorts. This is called HEADROOM. Home equipment often has a HEADROOM of +3 dB, meaning that when the meter hits +3 dB, your sound distorts. Professional gear can often go as high as +12 dB before it distorts.

Don't be a scaredy-cat and adjust your volume levels too low. Your recordings will have to be played back at a higher level to compensate, which will magnify the hiss, hum, and other electronic noise that accompanies every audio signal. You'll get your sound, but it won't be as clean as it could be.

SOUND MIXING TECHNIQUES

THE BASICS

A mixer is generally connected to an amplifier, recorder, or headphones. Connect the inputs to the mixer *before* turning it on. Sometimes when you connect up a device, there is a loud burst of sound when the plug is inserted. This loud *buzz* or *thlump* may come out of your mixer at full volume by accident. If your amplifiers or recorders *also* happen to be at a high volume, they will get a tremendous blast, which could tear up your loudspeakers or semipermanently magnetize your tape machine's RECORD HEADS, making it necessary to DEMAGNETIZE them (process described in the Maintenance chapter).

After connecting everything, it's time to test it out. Have your first performer speak or sing into the first mike as you adjust the volume level while looking at the meter. You want the meter to dance around the middle of its range but not go into the red very often.

Don't test your mike and volume settings by having someone say "testing 1, 2, 3 . . . testing 1, 2, 3." People never say this at a normal volume. Instead, have your performer recite a poem or say her ABC's at normal speaking volume. Trust that when the actual performance begins, the person will speak louder than during the test.

Once that input's level is correctly set, turn the volume OFF so that it doesn't confuse the issue when you are studying the next volume level. Repeat the process for the next volume control, continuing with each input to the mixer.

Repeat the same process for the high-level inputs such as the tape player and phonograph. Play each source and adjust its volume, jotting down proper audio levels for each if they are different. Some people place a mark on the level control that reminds them how far to turn up the volume. The trick here is to *test* all your sources and adjust their volume levels properly *before* the show starts.

When the time comes to do your show or make your recording, you may start with your volume controls already up and then cue your performers to start speaking or start your record, CD, or tape deck playing. If you cannot find a silent place before the music or speech starts, then you may wish to slowly fade up the volume while the music plays so that the sound doesn't start suddenly. Once your performers are speaking and your music playing, keep an eye on the audio-level meters.

Try not to "knob twiddle" too much. Loud bursts of sound come and go; that's normal. What drives people crazy is sound volume that goes up and down, up and down, so they have to jump from their comfy chairs and turn the volume down and up, down and up, when playing back your tape.

When adjusting volume controls for an auditorium or gynmasium speech, you will constantly be fighting the feedback gremlins. Keep the volume low enough so that you don't get a *screech* or *whoop* from the loudspeakers or a faint ringing in the room, heard at the edge of feedback. Selecting and placing your microphone and how you orient your speakers and adjust your volume controls largely determine whether you have feedback or not. When the room fills with people, the echoes in the room will decrease, allowing you to turn your volume up more without getting feedback. You'll probably have to turn your volume up anyway because you are competing with the noise of shuffling feet and squabbling children.

AUDITION OR CUE

Say you wish to play a sound effect of *boing* while someone winds his watch. How do you find the specific groove in your sound effects record that has the *boing* without having your audience hear you search for it? You cannot have your listeners hear you play *heehaw, meow, cluck cluck,* and *plop* as you seek out the *boing.* You would like to play these selections to *yourself,* find the right one, get it ready to go, and then at the right time, play it for everyone to hear

This is what the CUE or AUDITION switch is for. Switching it ON allows you to CUE UP your sound in private, adjust your controls, and then flip the switch back to PROGRAM for all to hear when you are ready.

Say, for example, your show is rolling along and you wish to set up the musical ending. If the music is on a record player, you turn the PHONO input to CUE and drop the needle into what you think is the right groove. You (not the audience, not the recorder) listen to the musical selection on your mixer's CUE SPEAKER or on your HEADPHONES. When you've located the appropriate selection, stop the record player and switch CUE to OFF or PROGRAM. (You may wish to turn the PHONO POT down first so that you can FADE UP the music when the time comes; if you leave the level up high, the music will start abruptly.)

SEGUE

SEGUE (pronounced SEG-way) is a fade from one sound to another: the sound of a crowd, for instance, smoothly replaced with music. The crowd's volume control is lowered at the same time that the music's volume control is raised. This is often done between two musical selections: as one finishes, the other is faded up.

A more sophisticated SEGUE uses an intermediate sound when changing from one audio passage to another. For instance, going from one scene in a radio play to another scene with talking, followed by music, followed by new people talking—you would manage by fading up the music during the performer's last line, turning off the volume after the line has been delivered, turning on the volume for the new performers, and then cuing them to speak while fading down the music.

Brief jokes or single statements may deserve a quick effect—laughter, applause, or a single note or chord of music between them. Such a musical passage is called a STING. Here you don't really need to turn down anybody's microphone, you just add the new music to a pause in their speech.

Some SEGUES prepare the listener for things to come like faint machinery noise before we open the engine room door, or the sound of windshield wipers before the actors begin to speak in the car on a rainy night. The SEGUE, a creative way to join two scenes together, makes transitions smooth and provides continuity.

MUSIC UNDER, VOICE-OVER

When doing the audio for a TV production, say your show begins with a snappy musical selection. The title fades in and then dissolves to the opening scene. Someone is about to speak. The music fades down just before the first words are heard. This is a MUSIC UNDER. The music became subordinate to the speech and is played *under* it.

Sometimes you have to decide whether to fade the music out entirely when the action starts or to keep it in the background throughout the scene (MUSIC UNDER). If the music is for dramatic effect, either to create a mood or to provide continuity through long gaps in action or conversation, then keep it in. If, however, the action or conversation is important, don't distract your audience with background music.

How loud should your background music be? It depends on the particular situation; there is no hard rule. Keep in mind that background music is *background* music: keep the volume low—lower than your natural inclinations. How many amateur productions have you sat through, straining to hear the dialogue through that "noise" in the background?

Use your VU meter as a guide to proper volume setting. If your narration makes your needle wiggle around 0 dB, the background should be about –8 dB, about one-fourth as high on the meter scale as the narration or action.

Songs with words compete with narration for the viewer's attention, so it's best to avoid them in favor of instrumentals. Songs with words do fit in nicely when you have no narration, such as when the actor is traveling, thinking, building, or otherwise not saying anything.

Music isn't the only sound that you can insert in the background. Sound effects, recordings of street sounds, machines, sirens, motors, and gunfire all add realism to your program. Some sounds might not be background at all but are interjected between dialogue, such as *thud* or *crash*. How these sound effects and backgrounds are woven together is called the SOUND MIX, and it's the audio person's job to mix them effectively.

Sometimes you are handed a videotape or film and told to add narration. The original sound on the tape will become background for the narration. Adding narration is called a VOICE-OVER. The voice you are adding is imposed over, and is louder than, the original sounds. (See Figure 5-1.)

For instance, Mr. Fixit brings in a tape of his repair shop in action—busy machines grinding and sawing away. Mr. Fixit also brings a script that he wishes to read during the recording. To do this, set up a videocassette recorder to copy his original tape from a videocassette player. The player's video goes directly to the recorder. The audio from the player goes to a mixer. Mr. Fixit's microphone also feeds into the mixer. The mixer combines and regulates the two sources and feeds the combination to the recorder. As the videocassette player plays, the videocassette *recorder* records, copying the picture and whatever original sound the mixer lets through. Mr. Fixit reads his script keeping one eye on the player's monitor screen. You adjust audio levels, sometimes favoring the background sounds (when the narrator is silent) and sometimes lowering them (when the narrator speaks). This is a VOICE-OVER. If Mr. Fixit doesn't like the way the final tape comes out, you can erase it and do it over because his original tape was not altered in the process.

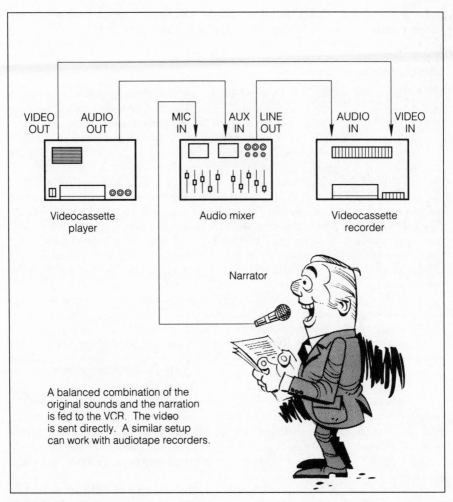

VIDEO OUT | AUDIO OUT

MIC IN | AUX IN | LINE OUT

AUDIO IN | VIDEO IN

Videocassette player

Audio mixer

Videocassette recorder

Narrator

A balanced combination of the original sounds and the narration is fed to the VCR. The video is sent directly. A similar setup can work with audiotape recorders.

FIGURE 5-1 Voice-over setup for VCRs

It is even possible for the script to be narrated from far away or long ago. You'll need a videocassette with background sounds and an audiocassette with the narrator's story. The process is about the same except that an audiocassette player provides the narration rather than a live person. Instead of the narrator slowing down, speeding up, or stopping his reading to coincide with the picture on the videocassette player's monitor, *you* must start and stop the audiocassette player to coincide with the pictures. If you have the script or have memorized the narration, you will be able to choose good places to pause the audiotape without catching the narrator between words.

MIKING SEVERAL SPEAKERS AT ONCE

Five people are sitting at a table, each with their own microphone; if you turned all the microphones on at the same time, you not only would hear one person speaking but you would hear the breathing and shuffling of the others. You would also get the hollow echo of the speaker as his or her voice is picked up on everybody else's microphone.

To avoid this problem, turn down all the inactive mikes, allowing only the speaker's mike to be live. This is easy in a scripted production like a newscast or a play but difficult in a free discussion. You never know when somebody is going to speak. One solution might be to *lower* by a third or a half the unused microphone volumes, raising each when the person begins speaking. Although the person's first words may be weak, they will still be audible and will soon be up to full volume. Allow the dynamics of the discussion to be your guide. If the discussion is a cross fire from everyone, keep all the mikes open. If someone seldom speaks, lower that mike. If one person seems prone to long monologues, take a chance and turn down the other mikes. Here the audio person needs to be very alert, keeping his or her fingers on each volume control so as to respond instantly.

CUING A RECORD

You wish to push a button and have that *boing* happen instantaneously, right in sync with the action of the performer as he winds his watch. Once you find the *boing* on the record disc, you need to get it backed up to just before the *boing* so that it will play the instant the switch is thrown. If you leave too much space before the *boing*, when you play it during the production, you'll get . . . boing. That's too late. If you don't back it up far enough, you'll get . . . ng, the tail end of the sound, or *wooing*, the sound of the turntable picking up speed while the effect is being played.

Professional turntables are designed to be CUED UP. They can be operated forward or backward so that the sound can be run backward searching for the silence before the sound. That's where you want to park the record ready to go. It's a little tougher trying to do this on a home record player; some don't want to be run backward, and others take a long time to get up to speed. You may have to experiment with several turntables to find one that will be CUEABLE. Table 5-1 details the steps for CUING UP a record.

Cuing up other devices requires a similar technique. Since some machines don't run backward, you may be required to play forward to the desired sound, stop, rewind a speck, play again, and by trial and error find the beginning of the desired passage. This is the technique to use for cuing a compact disc, an audiocassette player, or a VCR. One machine that *can* be accurately CUED UP is the old-fashioned reel-to-reel tape recorder.

CUING A REEL-TO-REEL TAPE RECORDER

This technique differs from CUING a turntable only in the mechanics. Switch your mixer to CUE and play the tape. When you get to *boing*, stop the tape, back up just an inch or so before the sound began, and leave the tape paused there ready to play. Switch the mixer to PROGRAM and hit PLAY when the time comes. Most professional reel-to-reel recorders have special levers and tape threading to simplify the CUING process.

Let's go through this process step by step:

1. Before the show or while your mixer is in the CUE mode, play the tape until you come to the *boing*.
2. Find the beginnng of the *boing*.

TABLE 5-1 Cuing a record

Switch mixer to CUE mode.	. . .
Play record forward in a search for the sound effect.	*cluck, cluck . . . plop, plop . . . boing, boing*
Lift needle and back up a couple of grooves.	. . .
Play the record.	*- - lop, plop . . .*
Get ready to stop the record.	. . .
Stop the record at the first sound.	*. . . boin - - -*
Rotate the record counter-clockwise to find the beginning of the sound.	*gniob . . .*
Rotate the record clock-wise to find the beginning of the sound, then back-ward again, eventually finding the starting *b* in *boing*.	*. . boi - - -* *- - - iob . . .* *. . bo - -* *- - - b . . .* *. . . b - - -*
Rotate the record backward an extra one-eighth turn.	*- - b . . .*
Leave the turntable in that position.	. . .
Switch the turntable's input on the mixer from CUE to PROGRAM.	. . .
At the appropriate time, start the turntable.	*boing*
Switch off the sound before you come to the next sound effect.	. . .

a. When you find *boing,* press PAUSE on your tape player.

b. While on PAUSE, place your hands on the two tape reels and manually back the tape up a little. You will probably be able to hear it play backward as you move the tape.

c. When you reach the *b* in *boing,* move the tape just a little further back so that the tape machine has some start-up time.

3. Switch your mixer to PROGRAM. When the appropriate time comes, press PLAY on your audiotape player or UNPAUSE it. Out will come *boing*. (Don't forget to kill the sound afterward or you'll catch a *cluck-cluck* too.)

If you are using a true sound effects tape, a quiet space between effects will allow you to park your tape recorder without catching the adjacent sound effects. If yours is a homemade tape, you may have to play around to catch as much silence as you can between the previous sound and the desired sound. Incidentally, if recording sound that you intend to edit later, use the fastest tape speed you can—7-1/2 inches per second or 15 inches per second if your machine will go that fast. This places more space between the sounds and makes it easier to CUE the tape.

MIXING SOUND WITHOUT A MIXER

If the name of your company is Pete's Poverty Productions, Inc., and you don't own a mixer or you perform sound mixing so rarely that it doesn't warrant buying one, here are some tricks.

Acoustical Mixing

Driving through the panoramic Rocky Mountains you want to make a videotape of the scenery, perhaps shooting through the windshield of your car as it winds along treacherous turns at the edge of steep ravines (have someone else do the driving while you do the shooting). You'd like to narrate your travelogue and have some majestic music in the background, but because you are only sending it to Uncle Harold in New Jersey, you don't want to make a big deal of this production. You could tune your car radio to a classical station, pull the camera trigger so that it starts recording, and talk while you shoot, turning the radio's volume up and down to "fill" in when you are not speaking. If your car has a cassette deck, that may be even better.

Similarly, you can DUB in narration and musical backgrounds later, perhaps in your hotel room or after you return home. Simply find a record player or tape deck and select the appropriate music. Set up your mike (or the mike in the camera; most can make AUDIO DUBS even if the camera isn't recording any new picture) close to you and the phonograph. The closer the speakers are to your microphone, the less room echo you'll pick up. Perhaps start with the music at normal volume and then fade it down while you begin your narration. Fade it back up when you finish speaking or during pauses. Although your sound fidelity won't win any prizes, the music and voice mix will make your tape seem quite professional. It's also rather exciting to play DJ as you try to coordinate switching on the VCR, starting the music, fading the volume, and making sense as you narrate your travelogue. Tape is erasable, so if you make a mistake or your sound mix is poor, you can do it over (and over and over, if necessary).

The appealing features to this method of sound mixing are first, it is very nontechnical; *anybody* can do it. You don't need any wires or electrical experience. Second, it's quick and easy, requiring no special equipment. Third, adding music or background sounds to a narration gives it color and professionalism. Most folk won't hear the difference between professional and amateur sound techniques but will appreciate the *effect* of mixed sound. Put another way, you add a lot of pizzazz for very little investment.

FIGURE 5-2
Y-adapter

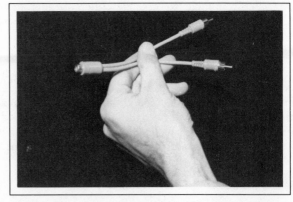

The same technique works for narrating audiocassettes. Simply turn on the radio, phonograph, CD, or music box while you narrate your piece. Your ear will tell you how loud to turn up the music and how loud to speak, but sometimes the mike hears things a little differently so make a short test recording to see how it sounds.

Y-adapter

This little widget (Figure 5-2) has three plugs or sockets on it with the wires tied together. Using it, one audio signal can be sent to two places or two audio signals can be combined to go to one place. You can also take two similar microphones, plug them into the two sockets on a Y-ADAPTER, and then plug the other end of the ADAPTER into your MIC IN, which allows you to use two mikes at once. You can use the same trick on audiocassette players, phonographs, or radio tuners. This technique comes with no moneyback guarantee; the connection may give your sound hum, hiss, or distortion. Figure 5-3 shows a possible hookup using a Y-ADAPTER.

SETTING PROPER AUDIO LEVELS BETWEEN DEVICES

Say you wanted to record your own telephone answering tape. You could do it on the telephone answering machine with its cheesy sound or you could mix some sound effects and music together with your voice and make a fancy high-fidelity answering tape. When you set up your equipment, however, you notice that your music source has a volume control, your mixer has an input volume control and a master volume control for the output, and your recorder has a volume control. At what level should you place all these volumes? The answer is to try to place them in the middle of their ranges so that each machine does its share of the job. You don't want one volume control at the top of its range while the other is at the bottom.

Start out by setting up your mixer. Plug in your mike, do a sound check, and adjust the mike's volume control to make the mixer meter happy. Ideally, the mixer's master output should be set at three-fourths and the mike's volume control at three-fourths. If the mixer says the signal is too strong, turn them both down a little. Next, plug the mixer into the tape recorder's LINE IN, press RECORD/PAUSE, and adjust the tape recorder's volume control so that *its* meters are happy. Now go back to your sound sources that have volume controls and feed their signals into the mixer. Adjust each to half volume

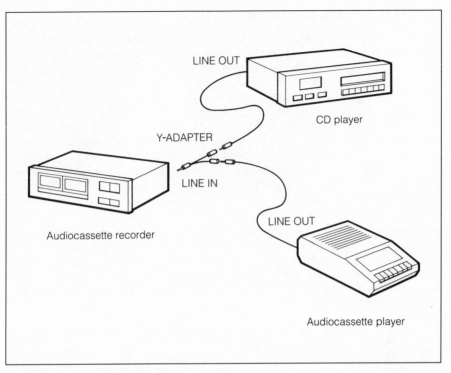

FIGURE 5-3   Mixing with a Y-adapter

and the mixer to half volume and see what you get. If the mixer's meter reads too high, turn both volumes down some. If they both read less than one-quarter volume, you may need an ATTENUATOR to reduce the signal strength from the source to the mixer. Continue this process for any other sources you wish to mix.

Tone Oscillators

Some mixers make this process very easy by having a built-in TONE OSCILLATOR or TONE GENERATOR. Instead of talking into the mike and watching a wobbly needle, you throw a switch that creates an even tone (probably 1,000 Hz). Flip the switch to turn on the tone, adjust the mixer's volume control for exactly 0 dB, switch your recorder to RECORD/PAUSE, and adjust *its* volume for 0 dB. The two machines are now *calibrated*. Whatever one meter does, the other meter will do. Next, turn the TONE GENERATOR off and adjust your mixer's volume controls for each input while attending to the mixer's meter only.

   If your mixer doesn't have a TONE OSCILLATOR, for about $34 you can buy a tiny toy keyboard synthesizer and set it to make a continuous tone. Feed the tone into your mixer, set it at 0 dB, set your recorder at 0 dB, and thereafter the two meters will match. Remove the synthesizer and plug in all your other sources, adjusting only the mixer's input volume controls; the mixer's MASTER and recorder's volume control have already been set perfectly.

AUTOMATIC VOLUME CONTROLS

Automatic volume control (AVC or AGC) is often found on portable audio recorders or video recorders. The circuit automatically sets the right volume level—no muss, no fuss. You don't have to sit there adjusting volumes; you just plunk down the machine, press record, and let *it* take over.

The automatic volume control does a nice job where the volume of the source is generally steady. The AGC goes awry, however, when the sound is very loud or very soft or quiet for a while and then loud for a while. Say, for instance, you are recording a speech with long pauses between sentences. When the performer stops speaking, the AGC circuit "hears" nothing and slowly turns up its volume. Still "hearing" nothing, it turns the volume up higher and higher. Turned all the way up, the machine records every little noise in the room, shuffling, motor noise from the tape recorder, some electronically caused hum or buzzing, automobiles outdoors, wind, and fire whistles in the next town. Then the first syllable out of the performer's mouth is thunderously loud because the volume is far too high for speech and hasn't yet turned itself down.

Here's another example. Say you are using an AGC recorder for an interview in a blacksmith's shop. The performer speaks, everything sounds fine, and then somebody's hammer strikes an anvil. The AGC reacts by lowering the record volume drastically and then slowly raising it again to the level appropriate for speech. The recording would sound like this:

Under the spreading chestnut tree, the Village Smithy sta—WHANG!
. . . he . . . ith . . . and sinewy hands.
And the muscles—WHANG! . . . rms . . . strong . . . iron bands.

It would be better if the loud noise came and went in a flash, leaving most of the speech intact, like this:

Under the spreading chestnut tree, the Village Smithy stands.
The smith, a mighty man is he with—WHANG! . . . and sinewy hands.
And the muscles of his—WHANG! . . . arms—WHANG! . . . strong as
    iron bands.

As you can see, AGC doesn't like long silent pauses or short outbursts. It prefers a constant level of sound. Music that has quiet parts and loud parts is also wrecked by AGC.

There are AGC devices that react quickly to loud sounds and slowly build up their volumes during pauses. These are expensive and not built into the reasonably priced portable audio and videocassette recorders.

MONITORING AUDIO

Nothing brings good luck like not relying on it. People who constantly check their work don't get unwelcome surprises. During your recording session, your headphones should become part of your head and your eyes should be on the meters. If you are working in the same room with the musicians, use muff-type headphones that seal out direct sounds, allowing you to concentrate on what is being recorded and don't allow you to be distracted by the live sounds of the band. Wearing headphones, you can adjust the levels so that the volume of each performer plus the background music all blend together well. Meanwhile, watch the mixer's or recorder's meters to see that the volume is right. Your headphones help you judge the *quality* of the sound mix.

Monitoring your audio also allows you to track down sound problems. For instance, if you have microphones going into a mixer and the mixer feeding a videocassette recorder, the VCR could send its signal to a TV set with a speaker. What happens if you get no sound on the TV? Is it the TV's fault? the VCR's? the mixer's ? the mike's? Here is where meters and headphone outputs come in handy. If the mixer has a meter and the meter wiggles when someone speaks into the microphone, the mixer and mike are most likely working. If you can plug headphones into the HEADPHONE jack on the mixer, you can ensure that the mixer and mike are working. If the headphones and the meter are silent, then the problem is probably in the microphone or in the mixer. Try another microphone or check its ON/OFF switch. Maybe the mike's battery (if it uses one) is dead. Maybe the mixer has a switch in the wrong position or its MASTER volume control is all the way down. Maybe the mike wire is broken or plugged in wrong.

If your source is not a mike but is another tape deck, plug your headphone into the tape deck to see if the source's signal is okay. If you get no signal at the source, maybe your tape is blank. If you do get a signal, maybe something is wrong with the wire between the source and your mixer.

Once you've proven that your signal is playing through the mixer, turn your investigation to the VCR. Is the VCR's meter (if it has one) wiggling? If not, something has gone wrong between the mixer and the VCR. Are the two connected properly? Is the VCR in the RECORD mode so that it registers the signals going into it? Is the VCR switched so that it is "listening" to the right input? Is the VCR's RECORD VOLUME (if it has one) turned up? Is the audio wire connected tightly?

If the VCR's meter wiggles or if you've plugged your headphone into the VCR and heard sound, then your problem is between the VCR and the TV monitor. Are they connected correctly? Is the TV "listening" to the VCR? (VCRs have OUTPUT SELEC- TORS that send different signals to different places—the VCR might be sending "Wheel of Fortune" reruns to your TV.) Check your TV's volume control. Plug your headphone into the TV (if it has a HEADPHONE jack) to see what you get.

The best place to monitor audio during a recording is the recorder's HEADPHONE OUT rather than the mixer's HEADPHONE OUT. If you are monitoring sound from the mixer, you don't know if anything is going awry with your recorder. If you are monitoring the sound at the recorder, you will be testing *two* things at once: the mixer *and* the recorder.

Before Recording for Real

There's a saying, "When you pick up a cat by the tail, you learn something you can't learn any other way." The warning you are about to read will go unpracticed until the *big blunder* inevitably happens. Before recording something for real,

1. Make a test recording.
2. Play it back.

The playback is the acid test. It is so easy to hear sound on your headphones and see the meter wiggling and see the tape moving only to find out you hit PLAY instead of RECORD or your heads were dirty or your tape was bad or some switch was flipped wrong. An ounce of testing is worth a pound of stomach acid. Murphy's first law states that whatever can go wrong, will go wrong and at the most inopportune time. A compulsion for quality testing is the only way to combat Murphy.

AMPLIFIERS, SPEAKERS, AND
PUBLIC ADDRESS SYSTEMS

An amplifier turns medium-sized audio signals into strong audio signals that can be sent to a loudspeaker. Some amplifiers have built-in PREAMPLIFIERS that accept weak audio signals like those from microphones. A public address (PA) system is a specialized "industrial-strength" amplifier designed primarily for speech, high power, and long hard use. Its inputs and outputs are often tailored to the application that involves one or two mikes feeding several loudspeakers. We will discuss PA systems in more detail later. Let's start with the typical home-type hi-fi amplifier and its features.

Plain old amplifiers are sometimes hard to find unless you are buying an industrial PA system. Consumer amplifiers are generally integrated into tuners, turntables, and cassette players. A radio tuner/amplifier combo is generally called a RECEIVER. Sometimes amplifiers are integrated into the speaker cabinet, making an amplifier/speaker combo. This is often the way smaller guitar amplifiers are sold.

There are several ways to describe an amplifier. One is by its *power*, or how many WATTS of signal it can produce. The more WATTS of power, the louder the sound the amplifier and speaker can make. FREQUENCY RESPONSE is another measure of the quality of an amplifier and speaker. Ideally, the equipment should reproduce all of the frequencies the human ear can hear: 20 Hz–20,000 Hz. Another measure of a sound system's quality is its DISTORTION (sometimes called THD for total harmonic distortion). This measures how much the system mangles, exaggerates, or colors the sound going through it. Of course the less you have of this, the better.

WATTAGE

If you look on the back of almost any electronic device, you will see listed there the number of WATTS the device uses to operate—the measure of power *going into* the machine to make it work. Do not confuse this with the WATTS of sound signal an amplifier can *produce;* that's a different number altogether. A typical amplifier might use 100 WATTS of electrical power to run its circuits while producing only 4 WATTS of sound signal sent to the speakers. From here on when we talk about *wattage,* we'll be talking about the power that the machine actually sends to the speakers.

WATTS measures power and the more power that is sent to the speakers, the louder the sound will be. Portable radios and TVs generally have 1/10- to 1/2-WATT amplifiers. Industrial (school) record players and console TV sets run about 5 WATTS, enough to be heard in a classroom. A 30-WATT amplifier—recommended for control room and studio monitoring—has enough guts to drive a hi-fi speaker and fill a room with sound without distorting peak sounds. Auditorium and multispeaker public address systems need 100–500-WATT amplifiers to feed quality sound to hundreds of ears. For stereo sound, amplifiers require twice the power, such as 50 WATTS for the left channel and 50 for the right channel.

How many WATTS your home sound system needs depends on how loud you play it. For background music, 13 watts will do just fine; 1 or 2 watts will fill the room, leaving plenty of extra power for the boom of a drum or the poop of a tuba. If you are the kind of person who sits with your arms folded and listens to CDs, then you might appreciate more sound volume. For this, a 60-watt amplifier generally does the trick, but I'm speaking as a middle-aged person. Teenagers and true audiophiles enjoy their music *loud* and need amplifiers yielding 100 to 200 watts. This is enough sound to rattle the dishes in the kitchen, scare the cat off the back porch, and let the neighbors know you have a *big* hi-fi system. Even in the largest living room, 100 watts is deafening. Guitar amplifiers and other loud music amplifiers generally need to produce 100 watts or so because they are attempting to feed undistorted high power to large rooms with noisy audiences. Most power goes into the bass notes. The ting of bells and cymbals, although they may seem loud, use only a few watts. It's the low bass notes that suck up the huge power.

Public address systems, because they feed sound to large rooms or many rooms at once, need more power. They often have amplifiers running 100 to 300 watts and occasionally as much as 500 watts. Incidentally, the more watts of power that an amplifier produces, the heavier the amplifier.

You will remember no doubt from the science lesson in Chapter 1 that amplifier wattage and apparent sound volume are not *linear*—they are *logarithmic*, which means that 5 watts is *not* 5 times louder than 1 watt and 100 watts is not double the volume of 50 watts. A general rule of thumb is to multiply the wattage by 10 to double the apparent sound volume. This means that 10 watts sounds twice as loud as 1 watt and 100 watts sounds twice as loud as 10 watts.

FREQUENCY RESPONSE

For hi-fi listening enjoyment, you need an amplifier and speaker that will give you the full range of frequency response (20 Hz–20,000 Hz). Older people's hearing doesn't extend into the very high or very low frequencies and might be satisfied with amplifiers running 50 Hz to 12,000 Hz, as will the average person listening to background music. The fine standards of some equipment exceed the frequency response of the human ear. Specifications like the 5 Hz–25,000 Hz on some gourmet amplifiers amounts to overkill; no recorded music extends to these frequencies.

Public address amplifiers used mostly for voice and occasionally for music can get by with a frequency response of 50 Hz–15 kHz. Generally the mikes and sound sources that feed these amplifiers are less than ideal; the speakers may be low-fidelity ceiling-mounted speakers or heavy-duty built-for-loudness knockabouts capable of reproducing a limited frequency range. For PA systems you may find yourself spending more wampum on watts and less on frequency response.

When reading specifications on frequency response, watch for the part that tells plus or minus so many dB. A 3-dB drop at the high and low frequencies is permissible, but some low-quality amplifiers may start to drop off at 10 kHz and will drop off precipitously at the top and bottom ends of the frequency range. Figure 6-1 shows a power curve measured in watts for a fairly decent amplifier. Figure 6-2 shows the same power curve measured in decibels.

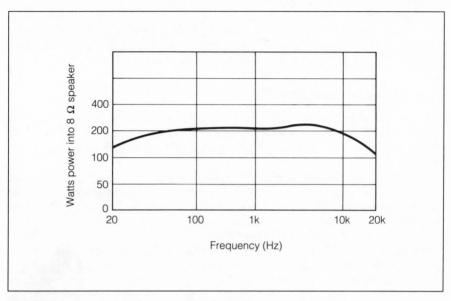

FIGURE 6-1 Power curve for an amplifier (in watts)

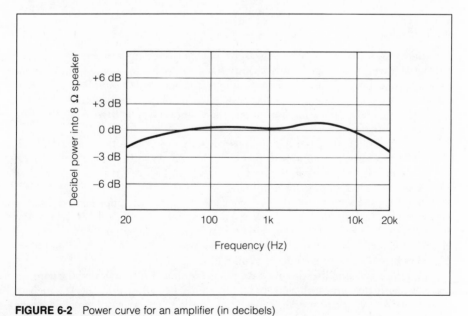

FIGURE 6-2 Power curve for an amplifier (in decibels)

DISTORTION

When an amplifier's specifications say that it puts out 50 watts of power at 0.25 percent distortion, this represents a true "clean" 50 watts of power. You won't hear the tiny 0.25 percent distortion. A 1 percent distortion level is not too bad, but 5 percent is unbearable.

Slightly different but still related is HARMONIC DISTORTION or THD (total harmonic distortion). HARMONIC DISTORTION occurs when you feed your amplifier a tone and it adds a little tone of its own, at one-half and two times the original frequency. Again, a 1 percent THD is livable, whereas 0.25 percent or less is excellent.

SIGNAL-TO-NOISE (S/N) RATIO

When you send a signal into an amplifier, you want that signal to come out of the amplifier unadulterated. Nothing should be added except loudness and nothing should be subtracted. Unfortunately, no amplifier is perfect; each adds a little noise of its own.

You want the most signal and the least noise. If you made a fraction using the signal strength as the numerator and the noise strength as the denominator, you would hopefully be putting a big number in the top of the fraction and a small number in the bottom of the fraction. For professional audio systems, this ratio reduces to a big number such a 55:1 or 55. This means that it is possible to produce 55 dB of sound before the system generates 1 dB of noise. Some people express this as a negative number (such as –55 dB). Either way, the bigger the number (or the more negative the number) the better. A 40-dB audio signal-to-noise ratio is mediocre, what you'd find on a non-hi-fi VCR or inexpensive portable audiocassette player. An S/N RATIO of 80 to 96 dB is typical of higher-quality amplifiers.

IMPEDANCE

Impedance—an electronic term—measures how much an input or an output resists the signal traveling through it. What's important is that the input of the amplifier has an impedance that matches the source feeding it; the output of the amplifier also needs an impedance that matches the speaker attached to it. We discussed input impedances in Chapter 2; now let's examine output impedances, which involve connecting amplifiers to speakers.

The output of an amplifier has an impedance that must match the impedance of the speaker to carry the signal with maximum efficiency. Most home speakers are 8 ohms and may have a label on the back marked "8 Ω." Thus, most stereo amplifiers for the home have 8-ohm speaker outputs.

Some amplifiers have outputs for speakers with different impedances. Smaller speakers may be 4 ohms, and a few speakers may be found with 2 or 16-ohm impedances. The more versatile amplifiers may have several outputs, one for each of the more common impedances—4, 8, and 16 ohms. If you have such an amplifier, Figure 6-3 shows how to connect it to an 8-ohm speaker.

Sometimes the amplifier doesn't have screw terminals for connecting the wire but instead has little clips with wire holes. In that case, remove about 1/2 inch of insulation from your two speaker wires. Stick one wire into one hole while pressing down on the little lever, which opens the hole, and push the wire in. Do the same for

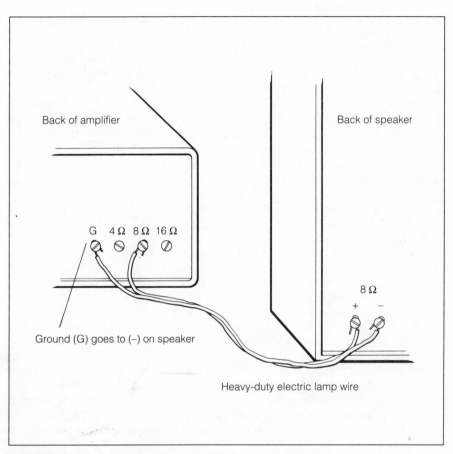

FIGURE 6-3   Connecting an 8-ohm speaker to an amplifier's output

the other wire. In the end, one wire will go to the red clip and the other wire will go to the black clip. The same arrangement is made at the speaker end.

SPEAKERS

A speaker consists of a coil of wire, called a VOICE COIL, attached to a paper or polypropylene cone-shaped diaphragm. When an oscillating electrical current goes through the VOICE COIL, it creates magnetism that attracts or repels a large permanent magnet built into the rear of the speaker. As this coil moves in and out, so does the speaker CONE, compressing the air around it and converting electrical oscillations into sound vibrations.

There are paper CONES, polypropylene CONES, and ice cream CONES. Paper is the cheapest and most common. Polypropylene is stiffer than paper, and because it resists flexing and buckling, it adds less distortion to the sound. It's also less massive than paper, giving it clarity in higher frequencies. Ice cream CONES make terrible speaker diaphragms and tend to litter your floor with crumbs.

Bass notes require that you move large volumes of air, so speakers designed for bass notes (WOOFERS) need to be quite large. A good WOOFER should operate in the 25-Hz–300-Hz range. Better speakers go to lower frequencies but cost a lot.

A MIDRANGE speaker handles the middle frequencies, about 800 Hz to 16,000 Hz. These frequencies are easier to reproduce and require less-sophisticated speakers. MIDRANGE speakers are generally 4 to 5 inches in diameter.

TWEETERS are tiny speakers (generally about 1 inch in diameter) designed to reproduce high frequencies such as 6 kHz–30 kHz. TWEETERS have tiny speaker cones with very little mass because it is hard to get something large to wiggle back and forth fast enough to reproduce high frequencies. Midpriced speaker systems—about $150 per speaker—generally offer a frequency response of 50 Hz–20,000 Hz. Figure 6-4 shows an assortment of hi-fi speakers.

When all three types of speakers are in the same cabinet, the result looks like Figure 6-5. Sometimes the speakers are behind a grille cloth so that you can't see them (or poke something through them by accident). The speaker grille is transparent to sound and is there just for looks.

It would be a waste to allow the bass sound signals to go to the TWEETER and the high notes to go to the WOOFER. Neither would produce any sound, yet both would soak up some of the power, thus wasting it. To send the right signals to the right places, the speaker contains a small electrical circuit called a CROSSOVER.

Less expensive than the THREE-WAY SYSTEM is a TWO-WAY SYSTEM, which uses just a woofer and a tweeter and a TWO-WAY CROSSOVER network. Here the sound is divided into low and middle frequencies that are sent to the WOOFER and high and middle frequencies that are sent to the TWEETER.

You don't *have* to have three or even two speakers to make sound. A single speaker will do a decent job as long as you are not expecting too much bass or treble from it. Called FULL-RANGE speakers, these are the plain inexpensive speakers found in common radios and TV sets. They are usually midsized so that they reproduce low notes and high notes adequately while reproducing midsounds (where most voice and music tones are anyway) excellently.

Enclosures

The box that you put a speaker in—the ENCLOSURE—is almost as important as the speaker itself. The sound inside the box resonates so that certain frequencies are fortified and come out stronger. To help these sounds come out of the box, an additional hole—a BASS PORT—is sometimes drilled into the front of the box. This hole is placed so that certain (usually low) frequencies exit the box in phase with the sound coming directly from the speaker. This often adds a nice deep bassiness to the speaker system, more bassiness than the *woofer* alone could make.

Enclosures are often shaped precisely and filled with acoustical material (sometimes fiberglass insulation) so that they resonate certain frequencies better. Often the speakers in the enclosures are *tuned* to work synergistically. Generally speaking, the better speakers are heavy and the better enclosures are also heavy. You can almost tell how good a speaker system is by how much it weighs.

Many enclosures are veritable rattletraps. To be rattleproof, the ENCLOSURE should be glued and screwed and each DRIVER (speaker chassis) sealed to the box with a gasket.

Tweeter

Midrange

Woofer

FIGURE 6-4 Assorted speakers

FIGURE 6-5
Three-way speaker system

Rap the cabinet with your knuckles. It should go *nick-nick* rather than a hollow, resonant *boink-boink*.

Frequency Response and Distortion

Like amplifiers, speakers are measured by how much wattage they can handle. A 100-watt speaker costs much more than a 5-watt speaker. Also like amplifiers, speakers work over a certain frequency range. That range can be graphed showing which frequencies the speaker reproduces well and which ones it reproduces poorly. The best graph would be a flat one, but no speaker or speaker system is perfect. Generally several speakers are teamed together to make up for each other's weaknesses.

Distortion is another measure of a speaker's capabilities. A speaker needs a very stiff cone that will not bend as it vibrates back and forth. Other mechanical attributes add to a speaker's ability to reproduce sound without distorting it.

Efficiency

EFFICIENCY measures how much of your amplifier's signal gets turned into sound by the speaker. An inefficient speaker wastes a lot of power and makes less sound.

Speaker EFFICIENCY is measured in dB of sound pressure level (SPL). The higher the SPL, the more efficient the speaker. An average speaker with an SPL of 90 dB will take a 1-watt signal and turn it into 90 dB of sound volume at a distance of 1 meter from the speaker. A speaker with a 98-dB rating would be considered excellent; one with a 79-dB rating, poor, as far as EFFICIENCY was concerned.

When comparing speakers, here's what to look for: if one speaker has 3 dB less of SPL than another, then you will need an amplifier twice as powerful to make the same amount of sound. If one speaker has 10 dB less of SPL than another, it will need an amplifier ten times as powerful. Thus a 10-watt amplifier into a 95-dB-SPL speaker sounds as loud as a 100-watt amplifier into an 85-dB-SPL speaker.

A high-efficiency speaker is not a "perfect" speaker. Generally speaking, the greater a speaker's EFFICIENCY, the larger the speaker must be. Unfortunately, small audio systems, which have the fewest watts to spare, generally come with tiny, inefficient speakers. The small wattage/small speaker combination is not a good one, although apartment dwellers are often willing to accept this trade-off.

An unhappy general rule is that the smoother a speaker's FREQUENCY RESPONSE, the poorer its EFFICIENCY. The better speaker designs absorb unwanted distortions, either acoustically (by cone and enclosure damping) or electrically (in a smooth working CROSSOVER circuit), but this also soaks up your sound. The more distortions your speaker absorbs, the better your sound, but the speaker is less EFFICIENT.

When selecting speakers, try to match them to your amplifier. If your amplifier has plenty of watts to spare, then go for the less efficient speakers that give better bass response and can handle the high wattage. If your amplifier is small, then perhaps the more efficient speakers will give you more sound, although you may lose some bass.

If you're buying amplifiers and speakers at the same time, here's how many watts you're likely to need:

Room size	Type of music	Amplifier watts	Speaker watts	Speaker efficiency (SPL)
Small	Chamber	30	30	80–90 dB
Full	Any	50	50	90–100 dB
Full	Any	100	100	85–90 dB
Full	Any	200	200	80–85 dB

Amplifier Connections

Before connecting or disconnecting speakers to an amplifier, make sure it is turned off. Some power amplifiers can be harmed by short circuits or lack of circuits while you are diddling around with the wires.

Connecting a speaker to an amplifier is fairly simple. The speaker generally has plus and minus or red and black connectors for the two wires leading to it. Similarly, the amplifier will have plus and minus connectors or red and black terminals for the two wires coming from it. The trick is to get the plus (red) wire at the amplifier end to connect to the plus (red) terminal at the speaker end. Although a speaker will work if you swap the wires, you want the positive wire on the amplifier connected to the positive wire on the speaker.

If the amplifier is small (say 10 watts) and the speakers are nearby (say 10 feet), it doesn't much matter what kind of wire you use to connect them, except it should be insulated (plastic-covered). Smaller audio systems often have speaker sockets on the back of the amplifiers and sockets on the speakers. The wires that come with such a system have plugs on the ends; just plug in the speakers to connect the system.

When the amplifiers get bigger (say 100 watts) and the speaker is farther away (say 30 feet), then you need wire that can handle more current. Although they make special speaker wire, inexpensive 20-gauge lamp cord (sometimes called zip cord) will do just fine. It's available at any hardware store and is cheaper by the spool (generally 100 feet or more).

If you plan to run more than 100 watts to a speaker more than 30 feet away and you're worried about the efficiency of your connection, use thicker wire that has less resistance to the signal passing through it. Again, you can buy inexpensive lamp cord, but get the thicker kind such as 18 gauge or 16 gauge. (The smaller the gauge number, the thicker the wire.)

When carrying high wattage, use one continuous stretch of wire rather than two short pieces connected together. The connection is not only a weak link in your sound system, but adds some resistance to the signal passing through it.

Your stereo speakers must all be IN-PHASE. A positive electrical vibration sent to your amplifier's outputs should make both speakers move forward together—teamed up and IN-PHASE. If you inadvertently swapped wires plus-to-minus on one speaker, when the amplifier pumped out a plus vibration, one speaker would come toward you while the other speaker would move away. The speaker moving away from you creates a negative sound pressure that cancels the positive sound pressure of the other speaker. The result is *weaker* sound, not *stronger* sound. OUT-OF- PHASE speakers give a hollow, thin sound.

So how do you make sure that the plus terminal on the amplifier is always connected to the plus terminal on the speaker? The answer is to look *very closely* at the wires. Notice that one strand of the wire has a ridge molded into the plastic insulation; the other strand is smooth and rounded. If you make the ridged strand the plus (red) wire at the amplifier end of your system, connect the ridged strand to the plus terminal of the speaker at the other end of the system. Make the rounded strand of wire your minus (or black) connection. See how easy that was?

Speaker Placement

If you are setting up stereo hi-fi speakers in your home, the speakers should be about 8 feet apart to separate the two channels. Face both speakers in the same direction so that they both push the air in the same direction at the same time, making the sound waves IN PHASE. Place the speakers so that one is slightly to your left and one is slightly to the right as you face them. This way the left speaker sends most of its sound to your left ear and the right speaker sends most of its sound to your right ear. Other people in the room will hear sweet music bouncing around the room, but some of the stereo effect will be diminished. Keep a clear view of the speakers; placing furniture in front of your speakers will muddle your highs. Figure 6-6 shows an optimal hi-fi sound setup.

If you move the speakers out a little way from the wall, they will give better bass sound. High sounds are very directional; if you place the speakers at ear level, you will hear the tweeters better. If you don't aim the tweeters at your ears, you may only catch the high tones on the bounce as they ricochet off a wall. Low bass notes, in contrast, are not very directional; you probably can't tell whether the kettle drum is coming from the left or the right speaker while the ting of the triangle is easy to locate. For this reason, don't place your speakers directly on the floor because the tweeters may end up too low where only your poor dog can hear them clearly. Similarly, try not to mount your speakers too high or your TWEETERS will shoot their sounds over your head. Wilt Chamberlain will be the only guest in your house to enjoy your hi-fi music.

If good bass is important, you'll need a larger listening room. The walls must be 20 feet apart to support the long waves of a 40-Hz bass note. With a smaller room, the bass

FIGURE 6-6   Stereo speakers set up for optimal listening

will sound muddy. To increase the bass in a rectangular room, place the speakers along the *short* wall so the bass waves have sufficient distance to propagate.

When setting up speakers for large audiences or auditoriums, try to arrange them so they do not feed their sounds directly back into the performers' microphones. Also place the speakers high over the heads of the audience and then tilt them slightly downward so that the speakers have a direct line to everyone's ear without anyone getting blasted or being in the way.

Horn-type PA Speakers

When loudness and outdoor ruggedness are paramount and fidelity is not, the HORN speaker (shaped like a horn) is appropriate. These speakers are mostly used for public address, speech making, paging, and background music. Most have a frequency response of 300 Hz to 7000 Hz, good for speech but horrible for music.

Subwoofers

It is hard to make a WOOFER work below 50 Hz. Frequencies lower than this generally require a special WOOFER called a SUBWOOFER. These huge, power-hungry speakers are generally built into footstools to make them compatible with home decor. These speakers aim straight down to the floor, and the sound exits between the legs of the stool. The aiming of the speaker doesn't matter because low bass sounds are not very directional. In fact, you generally connect both channels of your audio amplifier to the SUBWOOFER, which mixes the two together and blows the combination into the floorboards (a real treat for the downstairs residents). You are not missing any stereo separation because you wouldn't be able to hear it in the first place. SUBWOOFERS can produce sounds even lower than you can hear and are also good for cleaning the dust off the basement ceiling. Because WOOFERS are expensive, it may be cheaper to buy two midsized hi-fi speakers, which don't have big expensive WOOFERS. Then connect up a SUBWOOFER to your hi fi to reclaim those deep bass sounds. Professional SUBWOOFERS may even come with their own dedicated high-power bass amplifiers, which get the heavy woofing signals out of your regular amplifier (where they sometimes load it down) and send them to a specially designed high-power amplifier.

Before getting all worked up about the wonders of SUBWOOFERS, consider that most LP recordings don't extend much below 40 Hz. The lowest frequency put out by a musical instrument is 16 Hz (organ), and the second lowest is 27 Hz (contrabassoon). Next comes the piano at 30 Hz. Actually, when that piano note is played, it's the 60-Hz and 90-Hz harmonics that you hear, not the very weak 30-Hz fundamental (unless you are listening to loud music in a quiet room).

Thus, you may be wasting wampum chasing boom-and-sizzle bass speakers, most of which only go down to a "clean" 55 Hz. You might be just as happy with a Spica TC-50, which woofs out a 55 Hz but also has a great MIDRANGE (where most of the music is anyway).

Speaker Care

Did you know that a 30-watt amplifier can put out 50 watts? It happens when you turn the volume way up, allowing the signal to distort and create a lot of high frequencies. So guess what happens when you connect a 30-watt speaker with a 30-watt amplifier? The two work fine together until some knob jockey cranks the volume up, blasting 50 watts into the speaker, most of it high frequencies, most of it toasting your TWEETER. That's how you burn up a TWEETER.

Your best bet is to have a big amplifier but run it low, thus always feeding clean sound to the speakers. Also buy speakers that are rated for 50 percent more watts than your amplifier supposedly can make.

LOUDNESS SWITCH

Some hi-fi receivers and car cassette decks sport a LOUDNESS or BOOST switch. Throwing this switch boosts the bass about 9 dB. Why would anybody want to do that? Because of a psychoacoustic phenomenon called the Fletcher-Munson curve. When you lower the volume of your music, the bass *sounds* weaker than the other frequencies. By pressing the LOUDNESS switch, you boost the bass loudness up to where it *sounds* right again.

MONITOR SWITCH

Most stereo receivers have a MONITOR SWITCH that is useful when you are making recordings. Normally, your receiver listens to whatever input you have selected: tuner, phono, CD, cassette, or TV. If you connect your audiocassette recorder to your receiver, it records whatever your receiver is taking in.

The problem with this setup is that you are hearing the *source* while you make your recording, when you'd really like to hear how the cassette deck is handling that signal. You'd like to *monitor* the cassette deck rather than the source.

You can do that if you set up your deck as shown in Figure 6-7 and press the MONITOR switch. The source's signal now goes into the tape recorder, comes out of the tape recorder, and then goes to your speakers. If your tape recorder fouls up, you'll hear the result immediately on the speakers. Furthermore, if you press PLAY on your cassette deck, the music will play directly out of your speakers; there's no extra button pushing to tell the amplifier to listen to the audiocassette deck.

PUBLIC ADDRESS SYSTEMS

PA systems differ from regular amplifiers in that they are designed for speech, where loudness is most important and fidelity is not. There are also high-quality PA systems that are designed for theaters and auditoriums where loudness *and* fidelity are important. PA systems generally have bells and whistles not found on normal audio amplifiers.

Bells and Whistles

Public address amplifiers often come with built-in mixers so that two or more microphones plus one or two other sources can be mixed without a separate mixer.

A GRAPHIC EQUALIZER or ANTIFEEDBACK control allows you to select a particular frequency and reduce the amplifier's sensitivity to that frequency. Feedback sometimes results when a microphone is more sensitive to one frequency than others. Also the walls in the room may accentuate certain frequencies, imparting a shrill or ringing effect to the sound. With a GRAPHIC EQUALIZER or ANTIFEEDBACK control, you can reduce the offending frequencies and thus reduce audio feedback in your sound setup.

You can often guess what frequencies need to be reduced by listening to the sound from your microphone as you turn up the volume on your amplifier. If you hear a shrill ringing or squealing as a person speaks in the microphone, the feedback is caused primarily by high-frequency sounds. If you hear a low *whoop* as people move near the microphone or move the microphone, then your feedback is of a middle or lower frequency. The object is to use lots of volume but to avoid the frequencies that cause feedback.

Most industrial-use PA systems will have XLR connectors for low-impedance microphones and perhaps additional phone jacks for inexpensive, common high-impedance mikes.

High-powered PA systems often have protective circuits in them to avoid overheating or damage due to short circuits or broken wires. Some high-power PA systems have a special protective muting circuit in them that turns down the volume of the amplifier just after it is turned on or off. This saves the speakers from a loud *thump* sound when the amplifier powers up or switches off. Always take a moment to turn off the volume on a heavy-duty amplifier before connecting or disconnecting any inputs. Again, you are saving the speakers from a loud *thump* or *buzz* as you make or break the connection.

The better PA amplifiers have ventilated metal cabinets that keep the inside circuits cool and the cabinet from getting too hot.

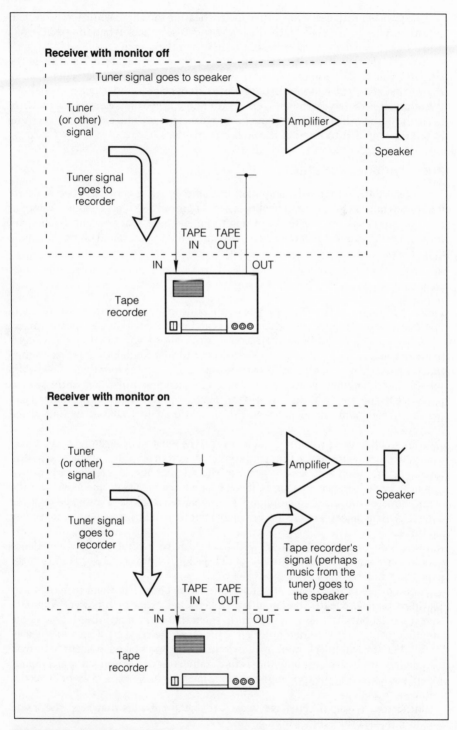

FIGURE 6-7 Tape monitor switch

C H A P T E R 7

BASICS OF
AUDIOTAPE RECORDING

Audiotape recording is a sport that anyone can get into. With a $30 portable cassette tape recorder you can document the goings-on at a wild party; with a million-dollar audio studio, you can record thirty-two musicians at once, mixing their instruments for just the right blend. Some mixing consoles and tape recorders are so complex that it takes a computer to operate all the controls. Some up-to-date professional studios have DIGITAL RECORDING equipment that can preserve the sound *exactly* the way it was performed, adding no discernible circuit noise, hiss, or hum.

Professional studios and postproduction houses OVERDUB, a practice whereby a performer sings a song on one track and the tape is then rewound and played back through the performer's earphones. The performer then sings harmony with herself and that harmony is recorded on another track. That tape may be rewound again and the talent sings a third track.

Another OVERDUB technique is to record the orchestral accompaniment in one studio at one time and later bring in the "star" singer to sing on a separate track while listening to the accompaniment playing from the first track. Thus a complex recording can be produced over a long period of time using people who have never met each other or worked directly together.

One step down from the professional studio is the "home brew" studio where a person prepares a room in his house with some acoustical treatment, making it into a studio. An assortment of affordable equipment connected together allows this "mini studio" to produce fair quality recordings for instruction, industry, or business. Many small bands set up such small studios to compose, record, and distribute samples of their work. Equipment has become so affordable that nearly anyone can set up their own mini studio for MULTITRACK RECORDING, OVERDUBBING, and AUDIO SWEETENING (improving the sound electronically, perhaps adding echo).

MAKING TRACKS ON A REEL-TO-REEL RECORDER

Common reel-to-reel audiotape can be recorded as ONE TRACK, TWO TRACK, or FOUR TRACK as diagramed in Figure 7-1.

Recording the entire width of the tape at once will give you better fidelity. It is also easy to slice the tape with scissors (or a razor blade) and cut out segments. ONE-TRACK recording is preferred by professionals.

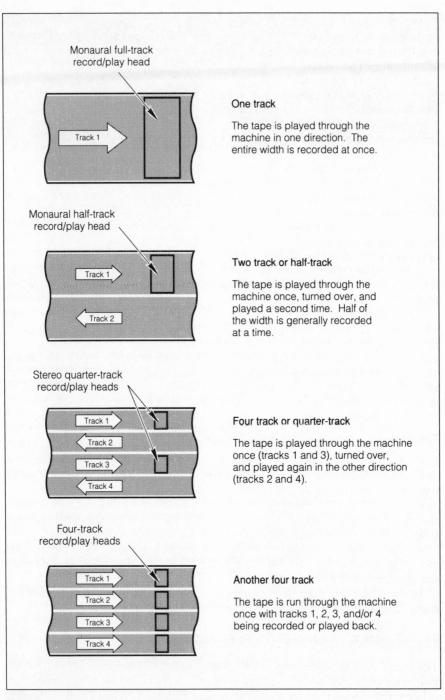

Monaural full-track
record/play head

One track

The tape is played through the
machine in one direction. The
entire width is recorded at once.

Monaural half-track
record/play head

Two track or half-track

The tape is played through the
machine once, turned over, and
played a second time. Half of
the width is generally recorded
at a time.

Stereo quarter-track
record/play heads

Four track or quarter-track

The tape is played through the machine
once (tracks 1 and 3), turned over,
and played again in the other direction
(tracks 2 and 4).

Four-track
record/play heads

Another four track

The tape is run through the machine
once with tracks 1, 2, 3, and/or 4
being recorded or played back.

FIGURE 7-1 Audio tracks on a reel-to-reel tape

TWO-TRACK (or HALF-TRACK) recordings were popular in the sixties. The audiotape recorder would record one TRACK over half the width of the tape. When the tape ran out, the full and empty reels swapped places and the tape ran through the machine a second time. The second half of the tape's width would now be automatically recorded. One problem with this system is that if you physically cut the tape to delete something from TRACK 1, you would be cutting two TRACKS, thus inadvertently deleting TRACK 2 as well.

A FOUR-TRACK (or QUARTER-TRACK) tape has four paths recorded down the length of the tape—two paths in one direction and two in the other. This setup is commonly used in stereo recording where TRACK 1 is the left channel and TRACK 3 is the right channel. When the tape comes to an end, it can be turned over and played a second time to pick up TRACKS 2 and 4. In short, two TRACKS are recorded in one direction with spaces between them, and two more TRACKS are recorded in the other direction filling those spaces.

A FOUR-CHANNEL reel-to-reel tape deck (recorder) can record one, two, three, or four TRACKS at once all in the same direction or two in one direction and two in the opposite direction, as described earlier.

Crowding four TRACKS onto a single tape decreases the sound fidelity somewhat, but it is still superior to any cassette tape recorder and satisfactory for anything short of professional commercial productions.

As with the TWO-TRACK tape, the FOUR-TRACK tape cannot be edited by splicing, which would cut all the TRACKS at once. This *might* not be a problem with FOUR-TRACK recordings where all the TRACKS contain exactly the same program, much like a ONE-TRACK recording. This means you could send your mixer signal to four inputs of a FOUR-TRACK recorder and make four identical recordings on the tape. When you play back all four tracks simultaneously and combine their signals, the sound will be just about as good as a professional ONE-TRACK recording.

The Difference between Channels and Tracks

CHANNELS are not the same as TRACKS. A TWO-CHANNEL tape recorder can make a FOUR-TRACK tape. The number of CHANNELS tells you how many independent signals the tape recorder can record or play *at the same time*. The common stereo recorder can simultaneously record one CHANNEL on TRACK 1 and a second CHANNEL on TRACK 3 while the tape is moving in one direction. When the tape is turned over, CHANNEL 1 and CHANNEL 2 will now impart their magnetism to TRACKS 2 and 4.

A FOUR-CHANNEL audiotape recorder can record one, two, three, and/or four TRACKS at once. You can also record TRACK 1, rewind the tape, record TRACK 2, rewind the tape, and so on for TRACKS 3 and 4.

In short, CHANNELS relate to amplifier circuits in the machine. TRACKS concern how many separate paths are recorded on the tape.

TRACKS ON AN AUDIOCASSETTE DECK

The tracks on an audiocassette recorder are similar to their reel-to-reel brothers. Except for specialized models, audiocassette recorders (ACRs) are two-channel stereophonic (two independent audio circuits). These ACRs can record four TRACKS on a cassette. Two tracks are recorded in one direction, and when the cassette is turned

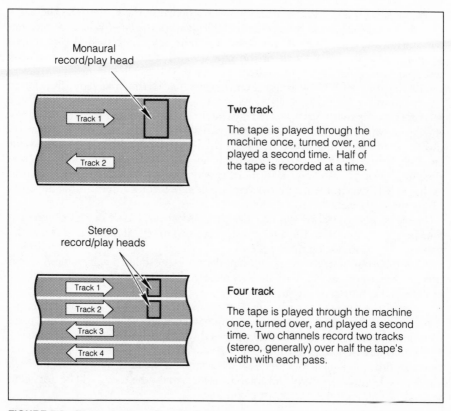

Monaural
record/play head

Track 1

Track 2

Two track

The tape is played through the
machine once, turned over, and
played a second time. Half of
the tape is recorded at a time.

Stereo
record/play heads

Track 1

Track 2

Track 3

Track 4

Four track

The tape is played through the machine
once, turned over, and played a second
time. Two channels record two tracks
(stereo, generally) over half the tape's
width with each pass.

FIGURE 7-2 Tracks on an audiocassette tape

over (side 2 or side B), the next two TRACKS are recorded. Thus there are four TRACKS on a cassette, but only two TRACKS can be played at a time. Figure 7-2 diagrams the TRACKS on an audiocassette.

Simpler and cheaper audiocassette decks that are monaural (not stereo) have but one CHANNEL and can record only one TRACK at a time. This TRACK covers half the width of the tape.

A four-TRACK tape recorded on a stereo machine will play back fine on a monaural two-TRACK machine. You will hear everything; it just won't be stereo. Similarly, a tape recorded on a TWO-TRACK monaural ACR will play back fine on a stereo ACR; you just won't hear stereo. Study Figure 7-2 to see how this all works. In fact, it works better for audiocassettes than for the old reel-to-reel recordings, where some tracks would play backward. In short, stereo and monaural audiocassette tapes and players are totally compatible.

TRACKS ON A VCR

Non-hi-fi videocassette recorders magnetize the sound linearly along the edge of the videotape as shown in Figure 7-3. Meanwhile, the spinning video head records diagonal stripes of picture across the tape. Monaural VCRs use one head; stereo VCRs use two heads, one for the left channel and one for the right.

Just because the signal is stereo doesn't mean it sounds great; it's still low fidelity because the tape moves so slowly. Hi-fi VCRs record audio linearly on the tape, but the sound is also invisibly coded into the picture. Because the spinning video head moves so fast across the tape, excellent fidelity (frequency response of 20 Hz–20,000 Hz) is achieved.

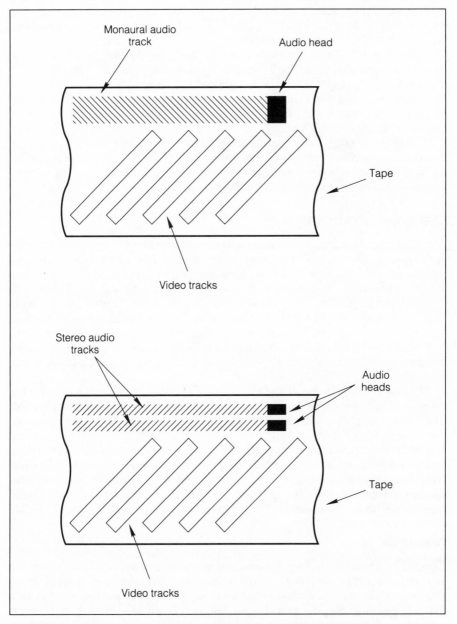

FIGURE 7-3   Audio tracks on monaural and stereo non-hi-fi VHS videocassette recorders

If you record a tape on a hi-fi VCR, you can play the tape on a regular VCR because the low-fidelity linear tracks are still there. Conversely, if you record a videotape on a regular VCR and play it back on a hi-fi VCR, you will still get sound (albeit not hi-fi). The hi-fi VCR listens to its linear tracks when it doesn't get a hi-fi signal from its video tracks.

When audio dubbing on hi-fi VCRs, be aware that if you dub in new sound, that sound will be recorded on the low-fidelity linear tracks, not the hi-fi tracks. You don't get hi-fi sound *unless you replace the picture too*. Furthermore, if you wish to insert *just* a new picture, your old hi-fi sound will be erased with your old picture (your old low-fidelity sound still remains on the linear track).

Thus, when videotapes are edited or audio dubbed, the "desired" sound is probably on the low-fidelity linear tracks. When playing such a tape, you may have to switch your VCR's AUDIO switch to the LINEAR position, *away from* HI FI.

To edit hi-fi tapes and preserve the hi-fi sound requires two hi-fi VCRs. Here you would edit the sound and picture simultaneously for each scene, copying them together from the original tape.

Hi-fi video recordings have excellent fidelity, exceeding all but the CD players and digital audiotape (DAT) players. In this respect, hi-fi VCRs make excellent audiotape recorders. As soon as you try to dub or otherwise separate the sound from the picture, however, your signal drops back to low fidelity.

REEL-TO-REEL RECORDERS

Although their format seems ancient, reel-to-reel audiotape recorders are still preferred by professionals. The better models provide excellent sound fidelity and can record and/or play back two to four separate channels of sound simultaneously. They accept various HIGH-LEVEL and LOW-LEVEL audio sources and can control their volumes independently. The better ones have two sets of record/playback HEADS which allow you to listen to your tape played back a fraction of a second after it is recorded. Listening to your tape this way lets you know that your recording is coming out okay.

Reel-to-reel tape machines simplify editing. The tape travels quickly and can be manually rocked back and forth, allowing you to play part of a sentence and sometimes even split words.

The tape is large (1/4 inch) and easy to handle, making it possible to use scissors to remove unwanted passages and to hitch the two ends together using SPLICING TAPE. Thus the content of an audio recording can be shuffled around, shortened (parts cut out), or lengthened (parts added).

Excellent consumer-grade four-channel reel-to-reel tape recorders are available for about $1,200. Professional reel-to-reel tape recorders may use 1/2-inch or even 1-inch tape and have eight, sixteen, twenty-four, or even thirty-two CHANNELS, allowing you to separately record up to thirty-two different sounds at once. Eight-CHANNEL recorders cost about $5,000; twenty-four-CHANNEL models, about $50,000.

Tape Speed

Nearly all professional and semiprofessional audiotape recorders (ATRs) move the tape at 7-1/2 inches per second (ips) for recording or playback. This speed yields excellent fidelity and fairly good tape economy—an 1,800-foot reel of tape lasts forty-eight minutes per side, yet still moves fast enough to leave editing space between words.

Home and semiprofessional tape recorders may have the 3-3/4-ips speed while professional decks may have a faster speed of 15 ips. The 3-3/4-ips speed has mediocre quality but excellent tape economy. The fast speed will get you only about twenty-four minutes per tape but spreads the sounds out, making them easier to edit.

Some ATRs have variable-speed (sometimes called variable-pitch) controls. Speeding up the tape raises the pitch of the music. This is handy when the piano you recorded yesterday is slightly off-key from the horn you're recording today. By adjusting the knob, you can slightly raise or lower the piano's pitch.

A second application for the variable-speed involves timing. Say you're trying to produce an advertisement that has to last exactly one minute. No matter how hard you try, every time you perform the ad, it runs one minute and five seconds. To get the ad to run exactly one minute, play the one-minute-five-second ad faster so it ends right on time. No one is likely to notice the slight increase in pitch.

Reel Sizes

Home ACRs generally use 5- or 7-inch reels. Professional decks can use 5-, 7-, or 10-1/2-inch reels. The big reels can record up to an hour even at 15 ips.

When using an ATR, it is a good idea to use the same size reel for both TAKE-UP and SUPPLY. If you don't, the machine will be unbalanced have difficulty stopping both reels at the same time after winding or rewinding.

AUDIOCASSETTE RECORDERS

Audiocassette recorders (ACRs) have poorer fidelity than reel-to-reel recorders. Editing on an ACR is quite difficult. Except to salvage a broken tape, an audiocassette tape cannot be SPLICED; it is simply too fragile. The tape moves so slow (1-7/8 ips) that it is hard to stop it between words or to CUE it up at a precise point.

One advantage of ACRs is that you can pop the cassette in and take it out with ease, even halfway through a song. It won't hurt the cassette to sit around half-wound.

Audiocassettes

Most audiocassette tape comes in three types: NORMAL, CHROME, and METAL. NORMAL tape (ferric oxide—FeO_2) is the least expensive and gives satisfactory frequency response. CHROME tape (chromium dioxide—CrO_2) gives better frequency response and is more expensive. METAL tape gives the best frequency response and, of course, is the most expensive. Any tape will play on any ACR, but the better ACRs have an EQUALIZATION (EQ) switch that optimizes the circuits in the machine to play a particular-type tape.

When recording, set the BIAS switch to the kind of tape that you are using to take advantage of the full potential of the tape. Thus, if you are using NORMAL tape, switch the BIAS switch to NORMAL. If you are using high-performance or CHROME tape, switch the BIAS switch to HIGH. If you are using METAL tape, switch to METAL. If you fail to throw this switch to the proper position, your machine will still make a recording; it just won't take advantage of the tape's full potential. In some cases, it may even cause slight distortion to the sound. Don't try to record CHROME or METAL tapes on a standard (no METAL or CHROME switch) recorder. It will sound worse than if you used the cheaper NORMAL tape.

Some tapes absorb high frequencies better than others. To match the machines to the tapes, use the EQ switch (if your ACR has one). NORMAL tape uses a 120-μs (microsecond) EQUALIZATION, so while using this tape, throw the EQ switch to the NORM position. When using CHROME tape (which has an EQUALIZATION of 70 μs), throw the switch to the CHROME or CrO_2 position. The cassettes generally tell you where to set your BIAS or EQUALIZATION switches.

Audiocassettes, like people's noses, come in various lengths. The most common lengths are as follows:

Type	Length of recording in minutes on one side	Length of recording in minutes for both sides
C-30	15	30
C-45	22-1/2	45
C-60	30	60
C-90	45	90
C-120	60	120

As you can see, the tape number tells you the total length of the tape in minutes.

The more tape you put into a cassette, the thinner the tape has to be. A C-90 cassette generally has thinner tape than a C-60 and therefore is slightly more fragile. A C-120 cassette has very thin tape and should not be used for anything except straight recordings and straight playbacks—from beginning to end. Trying to edit, wind, pause, and rewind a C-120 will eventually end up in a snarl.

Audiocassettes are of different quality. The cassettes you buy three for $1.00 in the supermarket will not give the same sound quality as those costing $4.50 each. The first cassette is probably satisfactory for speech, but the cassette SHELL (the package that holds the tape) may be poorly manufactured, which may cause the tape to snag in your machine. You not only lose your tape, but you get a tangle of snarled tape in your car's cassette player, requiring expensive open-dash surgery. For best results, stick to name brands. A higher-quality cassette SHELL is assembled with metal screws rather than glued together.

Prerecorded audiocassettes are a convenience, not truly high-fidelity media. Nevertheless be aware that there are *broad* differences in the quality of sound between brands. Nakamichi, Monster Cable, and Chesky Records Realtime cassettes have a good reputation. Avoid any cassettes that you see stored in the sun or heat; it's like buying a sirloin steak cooked yesterday.

Preventing Accidental Erasures

All audiocassettes have tabs in the rear, which, when broken off, leave a small hole that tells the ACR not to try to record (or erase) the cassette. Popping off that tab protects your audiocassette from accidental erasure. If a protected cassette is in your recorder and you press RECORD, the button will not go down or the RECORD circuits will fail to energize. If you're trying to record a tape and can't make the machine go into RECORD, examine the back of your audiocassette to see if the tab has been popped off. (Incidentally, videocassettes can be similarly protected against erasure.)

You'll notice in Figure 7-4 that the cassette has two tabs in the back. One tab protects side A; the other protects side B. The tab on the left as you look down on the label with the tape facing you is the tab for side A.

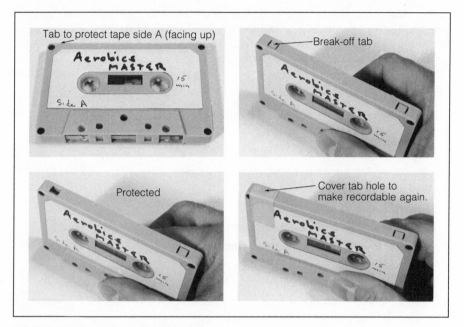

Tab to protect tape side A (facing up)

Break-off tab

Protected

Cover tab hole to make recordable again.

FIGURE 7-4 Protecting an audiocassette from accidental erasure

To render the cassette recordable again, place some Scotch tape over the hole where the tab was.

DIGITAL AUDIO RECORDING

All the equipment we have discussed up to now has been ANALOG: sound vibrations are turned into similar electrical vibrations that are turned into similar magnetic vibrations and stored on a tape. DIGITAL audio equipment, in contrast, converts the vibrations into numbers (1's and 0's) and processes or stores them. On playback, a DIGITAL machine converts the numbers back into sound.

Digital audio recording offers very high record/playback quality. When you record analog sound, imperfections in the tape and the recording mechanism damage the signal, so when you play back the tape, some of the waves get degraded or weakened, causing distortion in the sound. Also, the tape adds hiss to the background of the recording. If you make a recording of a recording, your SECOND-GENERATION copy will be poorer still, and if you make a copy of that copy, your THIRD GENERATION will really sound cruddy.

DIGITAL equipment, however, records 1's and 0's, which, even if played back with a slight distortion, are still 1's and 0's, allowing the mechanism to rebuild the original sound. Thus, every time you copy a DIGITAL audiotape (DAT), the degradation errors are corrected and your signal is restored to its original form. The big advantage of DIGITAL audiotape is that you can go 100 GENERATIONS without losing anything. The disadvantage is that storing all that data takes a lot of fancy calculating, requiring advanced recorders that are somewhat expensive.

No electrical device is perfect, and digital machines sometimes make errors and lose digits. Perhaps a piece of recording tape flakes off, carrying with it a few 1's and

0's. For this reason, digital audio equipment has built-in ERROR CORRECTION circuitry that tests itself and notes whenever the 1's and 0's don't add up right. The machine then fills in the empty spot with some digits stored from a few moments before. These patches in the sound generally cannot be heard.

SELECTING AN AUDIO RECORDER

Audio recorders are generally chosen for their features and their fidelity. The better audiocassette recorders may include

- DBX or Dolby A or C noise reduction
- Cue and review functions to monitor sound during fast-forward and wind modes
- Remote control
- Multiple inputs and outputs
- Equalization and bias switches to accept normal, chrome, or metal tape
- Balanced XLR audio inputs and outputs
- Tone generator
- Dual speed (1-7/8-ips normal tape speed or 3-3/4-ips high-fidelity speed)
- Automatic stop when in rewind if the tape footage counter reaches 000—good for finding the beginning of a musical selection

Reel-to-reel audiotape machines may have the above bells and whistles plus the following:

- Dual-speed operation, 7-1/2 ips for economy and 15 ips for high fidelity and compatibility with studio tape machines
- Switchable NAB or IEC equalization for compatibility with tapes recorded in the United States or overseas
- Removable head covers to facilitate alignment and editing
- PUNCH-IN recording, to switch the tape from PLAY to RECORD while the tape is moving, at the press of a button or foot switch
- Variable-pitch control that alters the record or play speed
- Simul-sync that allows you to listen to one track while recording on another
- Tape transport for two reel sizes, 7 inches and 10-1/2 inches
- Safe/record ready switch that protects you from accidentally recording (or erasing) your tape while you are absentmindedly punching buttons
- Headphone jack with selector switches that allow you to listen to any combination of tracks
- Rack-mountable chassis so the machine can be mounted in a standard 19-inch steel equipment rack with other equipment
- Fast rewind speed—the faster the machine can wind or rewind, the less waiting around you do

So much for bells and whistles; the list could go on for pages. Now let's cover some of the specifications related to recorder fidelity.

Frequency Response

Hi-fi VCRs and CD players and DAT recorders support an audible frequency range of 20 Hz–20 kHz. High-quality industrial reel-to-reel tape recorders reproduce 40 Hz–22 kHz ±3 dB at 15 ips. At the slower 7-1/2 ips, they generally reproduce 40 Hz–16 kHz ±3 dB. A double-speed audiocassette recorder is also likely to reach the 20 Hz–20 kHz frequency response, whereas a standard-speed high-quality cassette recorder is likely to reach 40 Hz–15 kHz ±3 dB. Using metal or chrome tape might boost this top number to 17 kHz; using standard normal tape may drop this number to 12 kHz. Non-hi-fi home VCRs running at the slowest speed, portable dictaphones, portable audiocassette recorders, and inexpensive AM radios work in the 60-Hz–5-kHz range.

Dynamic Range

In the middle of a live brass band, you would probably hear a 100-dB DYNAMIC RANGE between the softest breathing and the loudest trumpet player. The dynamic range, then, is the range between the softest and the loudest sound reproduced by the system. The 90-dB DYNAMIC RANGE available from CD players, DAT recorders, and some professional audio recorders is a near-perfect reproduction of this range. VHS and beta hi-fi videocassettes at 85 dB are also excellent. Even the 75–80 dB you get from an 8-mm videocassette recorder is very good and probably exceeds the DYNAMIC RANGE of the average hi-fi and speakers. Common tape recorders reproduce a 55-dB range, and portable audiocassette recorders and non-hi-fi VCRs reproduce a 45-dB range. The 70-dB range on many reel-to-reel tape recorders is adequate though not stellar. A notch below that is the 65-dB LP record. FM broadcasts have a 60-dB range while AM broadcasts have a wretched 40-dB DYNAMIC RANGE.

In short, the wider the DYNAMIC RANGE the better; aim for the highest number you can get.

Signal-to-noise (S/N) Ratio

Every electronic device adds a little noise (hiss, hum, distortion) to the signal that passes through it. In our quest for perfect fidelity, we desire the most signal and the least noise, which is expressed as a ratio of a big number (signal) divided by a small number (noise).

Before quoting an S/N ratio, you must examine how the measurements were taken. If the machine has Dolby or DBX noise-reduction circuits in it, those circuits were probably turned on when the measurements were taken, thus improving the apparent sound quality. The S/N ratio also depends on the kind of tape used: A high-quality audiocassette deck is likely to sport the following figures: 58 dB for metal tape, 55 dB for chrome tape, and 53 dB with a standard cassette. Generally, the Dolby B (described later) noise-reduction circuits improve the S/N ratio by 6 dB.

Double-speed audiocassette decks boast an 85-dB S/N ratio. Reel-to-reel tape recorders generally have an S/N ratio between 64 and 67 dB, depending on tape speed. Note that reel-to-reel recorders generally do not use Dolby to boost their numbers while the cassette machines generally do.

Wow, Flutter, and Harmonic Distortion

WOW is the *slow* wavering of a musical pitch; FLUTTER is a *fast* wavering, as if someone were shaking the singer. The less WOW and FLUTTER, the better. There are two measures of WOW and FLUTTER, WRMS and DIN. You don't need to know much about these methods except to use similar measurements when comparing specifications between machines. Compare a DIN number with other DIN numbers.

A good audiocassette deck will have a WOW and FLUTTER of 0.06 percent WRMS, or ±0.17 percent DIN. A high-quality reel-to-reel recorder may have WOW and FLUTTER figures of 0.1 percent at 3-3/4 ips, 0.08 percent at 7-1/2 ips, and 0.06 percent at 15 ips, measured the DIN way. Note that the faster speeds have less WOW and FLUTTER. Hi-fi VCRs have WOW and FLUTTER figures of 0.005 percent to 0.016 percent. When numbers get this close to 0 percent, you cannot hear any WOW and FLUTTER.

DISTORTION measures the sound the electronics make when you put a pure sound through them. DISTORTION, volume, and frequency are related; when a manufacturer lists a dynamic range and a frequency response, he should also list the DISTORTION present in the measurement. If one tape recorder has a frequency response of 20 Hz–20 kHz measured at 1 percent distortion while another has the same frequency response measured at 3 percent distortion, the first machine is better.

Reel-to-reel tape recorders generally have a total harmonic distortion (THD) of 0.8 percent (measured at 0 VU—full volume—and at 1 kHz). As you might expect, the distortion figures depend on the kind of tape used and the tape speed. A high-quality reel-to-reel tape on a good quality recorder is likely to give you a 1 percent distortion at 3-3/4 ips and about 0.6 percent distortion at 7-1/2 and 15 ips. Double-speed cassette recorders can achieve 0.05 percent THD at 1 kHz. Hi-fi VCRs have very low THD, 0.5 percent to 0.9 percent.

Anything below 1 percent is usually inaudible. The farther you go below 1 percent, the better *copying* and *overdubbing* the machine can do without adding layers of distortion to your recording.

Cross Talk or Separation

This measures how much signal from one channel gets into the adjacent channel on the machine. In other words, if there were a loud sound on channel A and no sound on channel B and you were listening to channel B, how much of channel A's sound would you hear? On most professional cassette and reel-to-reel recorders, you will find 40- to 50-dB CROSS TALK. The higher the number the better, as it represents more decibels of sound separation between the channels.

C H A P T E R 8

COPYING, EDITING, AND OVERDUBBING

This chapter deals with the pains and pleasures of copying tapes, editing them down to the program you want, and overdubbing—a technique for mixing several sounds together and rerecording them onto a single audio track.

COPYING A TAPE

Everything you hear today is a *copy* of something. Nobody ever distributes their MASTER, or original tapes, in case they become irrevocably damaged by the user. It is our copies by which we are judged, not our originals. A poorly made copy reflects on your entire work, so it's worth knowing how to make a good copy.

If you plan to make more than a dozen copies of a tape, go to a professional DUPLICATION HOUSE where they will make multiple copies for $2 to $3 a tape, depending on length and quantity.

If you plan to copy a program yourself, the process is fairly simple. You need a player, a recorder, and a patch cord to connect the audio output of the player to the audio input of the recorder. (If you are copying stereo you will need two patch cords.) Figure 8-1 shows some possible setups.

Before you begin, pop out the safety tabs on your MASTER cassette, eraseproofing it. *Do not skip this step.*

To make the copy, load your MASTER recording into the player and a blank cassette into the recorder. Check your MASTER cassette to see that its erase-proofing tabs have been removed—just as a precaution. If playing a reel-to-reel tape, cover the player's RECORD button with a strip of masking tape so you don't accidentally press it and erase a piece of your MASTER. Make sure your recorder's INPUT SELECTOR is in the proper mode to listen to the correct inputs (the ones connected to your player). Usually, you will be using the HI-LEVEL or LINE outputs from your player and the AUX, HI-LEVEL, or LINE inputs to your recorder. Use headphones to check on the sound quality from your recorder as it records.

The next step is to adjust your audio levels on the player and recorder. If the player has meters, adjust the output volume so that the meters jiggle in the middle of their range but don't hover in the red. If you don't have meters, turn the volume up about halfway.

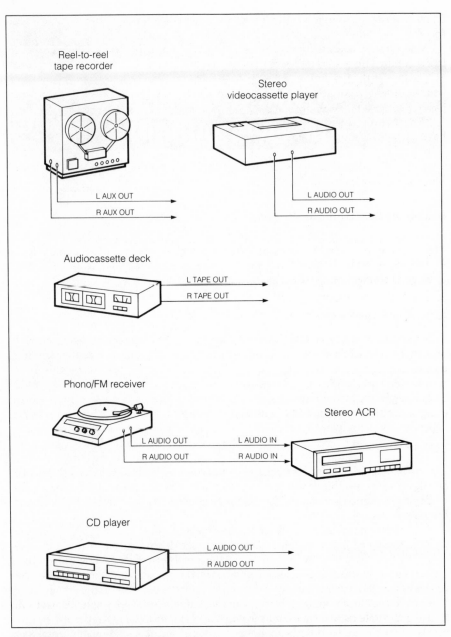

FIGURE 8-1 Recording stereo from records and tapes

On the recorder, press RECORD/PLAY/PAUSE, which activates the recorder's circuits but doesn't start the tape moving. Now the recorder's meters will help you see how to adjust the volume to make *its* meters happy.

After setting levels, carefully cue up the program you wish to copy. With a little luck, you should find a silent space before the program actually begins. Leave in a few seconds of silence so that you don't copy the sound of your music trying to get up to speed.

When you are ready to start recording, UNPAUSE the recorder and let it run for about five seconds. This gets *its* tape speed stabilized and also moves you past the unrecordable LEADER at the beginning of your reel-to-reel tape or audiocassette. At this point your recorder is recording silence while your player is on PAUSE. Once the recorder is past the LEADER, UNPAUSE the player and let the fun begin.

Now that you've successfully copied that tape, what do you do next? Sit down and have a smoke? Wrong! *You label the copy.* Make sure to put the word *copy* on that label. Copies and MASTERS look too much alike to be easily sorted out—but they are not *really* alike and should not be treated as equals. So label them and keep them separate. Besides, smoking is bad for your health.

Making the Best Signal for Copying

Copies never sound as good as originals. To make the best copy you need

1. The best player and recorder available
2. A good connection between the two
3. The best tape available
4. The right speed selection

Record your MASTER on DAT, hi-fi VCR, or reel-to-reel tape at the fastest speed. If quality is important, make your copies on these formats. Otherwise, do your mastering on the best format and your copying on an affordable format such as audiocassettes.

Use short patch cords with shielded cable or balanced lines if your wires must be long. Keep your connectors clean and tight. Use chrome or metal tape when possible, using standard (FeO_2) tape only for cheap distribution copies.

Selecting Tape

Use name-brand standard-length tapes—1,200- or 1,800-foot reel-to-reel or C-60 and C-90 audiocassettes. If you expect to edit, use more expensive professional high-grade tapes designed for heavy-duty use. Record your MASTER on virgin tape fresh from the box.

Protecting the Master

Label your MASTER clearly, pop out the erase tabs if it is a cassette, and keep your MASTER boxed in a cool, dry place.

MASTER tapes start to degrade after about one hundred passes through the machine, so make multiple duplicates each time you play the MASTER.

COPYING AND THE COPYRIGHT LAW

Nearly every recent commercially produced audio and video recording is copyrighted. Technically, it is illegal to duplicate this material or use parts of it on one of your own tapes.

If you are producing something just for your family and friends, no federal agents are likely to break down your door and carry you off to jail, so feel free to use whatever you want. If, however, you are making an industrial recording for pay, such as a training tape or product promotion, you must follow the rules. Get permission from the copyright holders before using any of their material. It is unequivocally illegal to copy records or tapes by the hundreds for resale without securing the copyright holder's permission. The long arm of the law will gleefully strangle you when it catches you.

If you do professional or industrial work, you may wish to buy a library of musical or sound effects tapes from a production house like Soper Sound, Valentino, De Wolf, or Associated Production Music. They sell you the albums plus the right to copy the music.

COPYING TV SOUND

Now that the sound quality on VCRs and TVs has improved, more people are interconnecting their hi-fi audio equipment with their hi-fi video equipment. Figure 8-2 shows several ways to set up an audio/TV sound system to allow you to listen to your TV shows on a $500 hi-fi sound system rather than your TV set's $3 sound system. You can also connect an audiocassette recorder to the system to audio record the sound from TV shows or video tapes.

Some of today's newer TVs can pick up stereo sound if the program is broadcast this way. TVs and VCRs equipped with special MTS (multichannel television sound) tuners decode the stereo broadcast signal and give you stereo sound. If your VCR or TV has audio outputs, you can also record the stereo sound on an ACR.

EDITING AUDIO

Editing is the process of assembling parts together to make something new. When you record the songs you like off the radio or a record, you are editing. To edit this way,

1. Set up your recorder and player as if you were going to copy some music.
2. Cue up the player so that the music will begin a few moments after the player starts playing.
3. Press RECORD/PLAY/PAUSE on your recorder so that it is ready to go.
4. Start both machines together.
5. When the musical selection is finished, press PAUSE again on the recorder.
6. Hunt for your next musical selection and start the process over.

If you are recording from the radio, it is hard to catch songs just before they start. To make your final tape smoother sounding, try this: before UNPAUSING your recorder, in step 4 above, turn the RECORD VOLUME down to 0 and then UNPAUSE. Next, fade the volume up to the right level. The result will be a smooth fade-in rather than the music crashing in.

Splicing Audiotape

If you want to cut a 45-minute speech down to a 10-minute speech, you can do just that—cut it. Quarter-inch reel-to-reel audiotape is the only format where this is feasible. (Cassette tape is too flimsy and is likely to jam.) Here's how to go about it:

1. Play the whole tape, taking notes on which parts are to be kept and which parts cut out.

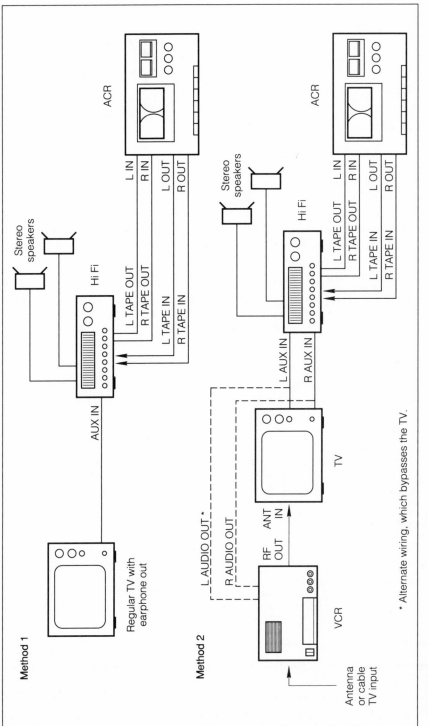

FIGURE 8-2 Connecting a TV sound system

2. Play the tape again, stopping it at the precise point where you wish to begin removing material.

3. Mark the outside of the tape (the side facing *away* from the audio playback head) exactly where it passes over the head.

4. Continue the tape until you come to the part you wish to include in your final recording.

5. Mark this spot.

6. Do this until you have finished the tape.

7. Now rewind the tape to the first mark.

8. Remove the tape from the machine and do the following:

   a. Using demagnetized scissors, cut the tape at a 45-degree angle or, better yet, place the tape in a SPLICING BLOCK and use the groove in the block as a guide to slice the tape at a 45-degree angle with a razor blade.

   b. Leaving the good tape in the splicing block, wind the unwanted tape off the supply reel until you come to the second mark (at the end of the bad tape and the beginning of the next good segment).

   c. As before, slice the tape on the mark and discard the unwanted tape.

   d. Butt the tail end of the first good segment up to the head end of the next good segment. They should touch but not overlap.

   e. Place AUDIO SPLICING TAPE over the junction and trim the excess. The SPLICING BLOCK will help guide your hand.

9. Continue this process until all the good segments take up a single reel of tape and all the bad segments are in the wastebasket.

Figure 8-3 shows the process, which can be done in any order. For instance, you could use the end of the orginal tape to begin your edited version. In fact, you can mix and match snippets from several reels of tape to make a single production of any length or order.

There are less-professional ways to SPLICE audiotape, appropriate when you are just trying to patch up a tape temporarily or fix a broken tape or if you edit tape once every Leap Year. The methods that follow are not perfect or professional but will get you by.

If you don't have SPLICING TAPE, use magic mending tape (best) or plain cellophane tape (okay). Common adhesive tape will bleed goo onto your audiotape over time and then dry out and come loose.

You can SPLICE audiotape or audiocassettes with scissors following the steps in Figure 8-4. Before beginning, make sure you wash your hands and use a clean sheet of white paper as a work area.

SPLICED audiocassettes have a tendency to jam. If an irreplaceable audiocassette breaks, first fix it as described above, then copy it. Throw away the master.

Pause Editing

Less accurate than tape SPLICING but still pretty good, depending on your equipment and dexterity, is PAUSE EDITING.

To PAUSE edit, you need a recorder and a player. Here's how you would go about editing a fifteen-minute speech down to five minutes:

To indicate the edit points, mark the tape where it passes over . . .

. . . the center of the audio playback head.

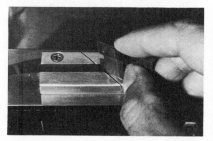

Cut the tape. Pull one piece away.

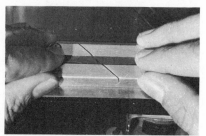

Butt two good segments together.

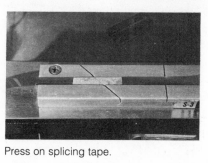

Press on splicing tape.

FIGURE 8-3 Splicing audiotape

1. Play the whole speech to determine which parts are to be kept and which ones cut out. (You may wish to take notes or type a transcript.)
2. Decide whether you want to edit the final tape in chronological order (the order in which it was said) or whether you wish to swap parts. Take some more notes.
3. Connect your player to your recorder so that the recorder can copy segments from the player. Also do a sound check, adjusting the volume controls appropriately.
4. Play the tape until you come to the first segment you wish to use. Back up the tape, play it, and PAUSE it a half second before the segment begins.
5. Start you recorder, first recording some silence at the beginning of the tape to get past the leader and also leave a little breathing space before you start recording.

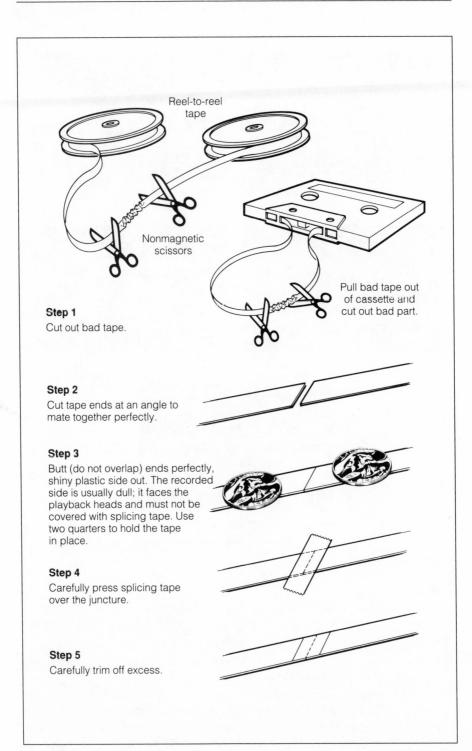

Reel-to-reel tape

Nonmagnetic scissors

Step 1
Cut out bad tape.

Pull bad tape out of cassette and cut out bad part.

Step 2
Cut tape ends at an angle to mate together perfectly.

Step 3
Butt (do not overlap) ends perfectly, shiny plastic side out. The recorded side is usually dull; it faces the playback heads and must not be covered with splicing tape. Use two quarters to hold the tape in place.

Step 4
Carefully press splicing tape over the juncture.

Step 5
Carefully trim off excess.

FIGURE 8-4 Splicing audiotape with scissors

6. Next, press PAUSE while the recorder is still in the RECORD/PLAY mode.

7. UNPAUSE the *two* machines simultaneously and let the segment play until the end of the first segment.

8. To stop the editing process, PAUSE the recorder (forget about the player at this point).

9. If you think you hit it just right, don't do anything with the recorder, just leave it in PAUSE.

10. Play the player up until the next wanted segment and PAUSE it just as the segment is ready to begin.

11. Repeat steps 7–10 until you have recorded all the segments.

UNPAUSING two machines at exactly the same moment is sometimes difficult. Another alternative is to rewind the player a little way and then let it play. Having memorized the point where the new segment should begin, as you hear the words building up to the desired sentence, you poise your finger over the PAUSE button of the recorder. When you hear the last word before the desired sentence, tap the PAUSE button on the recorder, UNPAUSING it. This method requires quick reflexes but probably sounds a bit better than the first method because the player is already up to speed when you start recording.

Still, the recorder jostles the tape a little before it gets up to speed, and your PAUSE EDITS may have a little squeak or click in them. Some recorders do this job better than others.

Punch-in Edits

Getting up to speed from the PAUSE mode is often a problem. The more professional recorders allow you to switch directly from PLAY to RECORD while the tape is moving. This is called PUNCH-IN editing and is very handy when you have flubbed a line and wish to go back and pick up recording just before the mistake.

Say you wanted to correct the line, "She looked right through me and didn't even say hollow." Here's what you'd do:

1. Rewind the tape a way.

2. Press PLAY and listen until, "She looked right through me and didn't even say . . ."

3. With your finger poised over the EDIT or RECORD/PLAY button, press the button when you hear "say."

4. Immediately say "hello."

The result should be, "She looked right through me and didn't even say hello."

Sometimes there are pauses in a sentence that are easier to edit between. You might want to go back and pick up at the end of the last sentence or after a comma where there is often a pause.

Insert Edits

Say you are recording a radio show featuring your favorite music. Then, the telephone rings and while you are away, a commercial gets recorded on the tape. You don't notice that the commercial is there until you play back the tape the next day. How do you get rid of the ad?

You could SPLICE it out, but you've probably recorded on both sides of your tape, making a SPLICE impractical. Or maybe you made your recording on an audiocassette where the tape is a little too delicate to SPLICE. Another solution might be to copy your tape onto another tape, PAUSING the recorder so that it bypasses the commercial. Unfortunately, this takes you down one more generation in sound quality.

The third option is an INSERT edit, which occurs in the middle of a recording, replacing one sound with another. INSERT edits are tricky. All common audio recorders will make an INSERT edit, but the more professional models do it more elegantly than others.

The process goes something like this:

1. Play your tape up to the unwanted segment. Jot down the number from your tape footage counter so that you can find this spot again.

2. Play your tape up to the point where the unwanted segment ends. Jot down *that* counter number. (You will want to start recording at the first number and stop recording at the last number.)

3. Go back to just before the first number and play your tape until the end of the last good segment.

4. Press RECORD/PLAY/PAUSE.

5. Find a program to insert in place of the one you are taking out. Technically, you could insert silence, but long silent passages are rather clumsy in the middle of a musical recording. Remember, you cannot simply take out the unwanted part of the program; you must *replace* it with something. Your recording doesn't become shorter, it just has one sound replaced with another sound. Locate some appropriate music or speech and prepare to copy it onto your first tape. If your new musical selection is longer than the commercial, you will have to terminate your recording prematurely or else record over (and erase) the beginning of the song that followed the commercial. Make your decision about which is more important, the new song you are putting in or the old song that followed the commercial.

6. Cue up the replacement song on the player.

7. UNPAUSE the recorder when the song begins and watch your tape footage counter.

8. When the counter tells you that the commercial is finished, quickly fade down the volume control and press STOP on the recorder.

9. Go back and see how it sounds.

Because of the position of the record and erase heads, the beginning of your INSERT EDIT has a second of old sound under your new sound. The end of your INSERT EDIT has a second of silence between your new sound and your old sound. Professional recorders place their ERASE HEADS and RECORD HEADS close together, making this pause very short, almost unnoticeable.

The hardest part of INSERT editing is the timing. If you are using recorded sounds, you have almost no control over when they end. You'd be remarkably lucky if you found a 55-second song to replace a 55-second commercial.

Working with speech, the process becomes easier. You probably have a script, and the narrator can speed up or slow down his speech to match the hole you are trying to cover in the original tape. You can lengthen the script or shorten it to match the unwanted segment. The process goes something like this:

1. Find the beginning of the unwanted segment and note the tape footage number.

2. Find the end of the segment and note *that* number.

3. Estimate the time of the unwanted segment and write the script to match its length.

4. Now conduct a dress rehearsal to test things out before irrevocably erasing your original tape: rewind to just before the first number and start your tape machine *playing*. When you reach the first number, cue your narrator to start speaking but allow the tape player to continue playing (turn down the volume halfway if the old sound is distracting). When the narrator finishes his script, check the tape counter (or listen to the original sound track) to see whether the narrator ended early, late, or right on time. Make any adjustments, practice again, and then prepare to do your insert for real.

5. Again, rewind your tape to before the first counter number and start the tape. Use the PAUSE or PUNCH-IN method when you reach the first counter number.

6. Cue your narrator to start speaking.

7. Poise your finger over the STOP or PAUSE button so that you can cease the recording process on schedule. Hopefully the narrator stops speaking before you have to press STOP, but if she goofs up and doesn't finish in time, it is better to press STOP than to record too long and spoil the following segment of old tape. As long as you don't cut into the following "good" segment, you can always go back and try this process again.

OVERDUBBING

As you get deeper into multichannel recording, you'll begin OVERDUBBING. An OVERDUB can be made on any multitrack recorder that is capable of playing one channel while recording on another. Many stereo and two-channel tape recorders can also OVERDUB.

OVERDUBBING is the process of playing back one sound channel and synchronizing an additional sound with it, then recording that combination onto another track on the tape. The process may then be repeated, adding a new sound to the combination and recording that mix on another track (perhaps the old first track, which isn't needed any longer). Thus you bounce back and forth from track to track, adding more and more sounds.

An advantage of OVERDUBBING is that if you mess up your recording, you can do it over. You haven't touched the original sound track; it is still there to be used again and again until you get your sound mix just right. Once you are happy with your mix, you may *now* sacrifice your original sound track and make a new OVERDUB onto it. Technically you need only two tracks to make a multilayered monaural recording.

One disadvantage of OVERDUBBING is that the hiss, hum, distortion, and other tape noise inherent in every recording adds up as you copy from track to track. Every time you go down one generation, your sound quality gets poorer.

Let's try an example with a two-track recorder. We want to record a 10-part harmony song using one singer.

1. First the singer sings the melody onto track 1. Then you rewind the tape and put headphones on the singer so that she may hear track 1. You may have to throw the SIMULSYNC switch on the recorder so that the record and playback heads are lined up one above the other, which makes the new recording occur synchronously with the existing music on the tape. (If another head were used, there would be a delay between what the singer hears and where the singer's new voice is recorded.)

2. Set up the recorder to record on channel 2 while it plays back channel 1. Adjust the volume levels so that the sound playing from channel 1 is recording at the right level onto channel 2. Make a sample recording if you need to, copying some sound from track 1 onto track 2. Once your levels are set, go on to the next step (which will erase the test on track 2).

3. If your recorder is equipped with separate volume controls for TAPE and MICRO-PHONE, note where the TAPE control was set and set it to 0. Now have the singer sing the second part of the harmony and adjust the MIC volume controls appro-priately.

4. Now go back and start all over again, this time turning up the TAPE and MIKE volume controls so that track 1 is recorded on track 2 while the singer's voice is also recorded on track 2.

5. Start recording. You now have two-part harmony on track 2.

6. Check it out; if it sounds good, dispose of track 1.

7. Throw your recorder's switches into the appropriate positions to record on track 1 while copying *from* track 2.

8. As before, do a test recording to make sure that the volume coming from track 2 is just right. This test recording is being done on track 1, leaving track 2 untouched. Note the volume level and then turn the volume off and test the singer's volume.

9. Once you know the right level for both volumes, rewind the tape and start recording again. The two voices on track 2 will mix with the singer, making three voices being recorded on track 1.

10. Repeat this process between the two tracks until you have all ten voices.

When you listen to the final version of the music, the first voice you recorded will sound muffled. This is due to the loss in fidelity from copying the sound back and forth from track to track. The best sound fidelity will be on the last recording you made, which is only one generation old.

This process becomes easier with a four-channel (or more) tape deck. Here you can record one voice on channel 1, go back and record a second voice on channel 2, and then go back and record a third voice on channel 3. Then go back and mix the volumes of those three voices, doing a test recording, onto channel 4. Once those volumes are set, you can set the volume for the singer and record him onto channel 4 while copying the first three voices from the first three tracks onto channel 4 simultaneously. Now you have four voices on channel 4, three of which are second generation and one of which is first generation.

You may now make another recording on track 1 (perhaps voice 5) and go back and make another recording (voice 6) on track 2.

Now we're ready to mix again. We play the sound from channels 1, 2, and 4 into channel 3, adjusting the volume controls to match the sounds. Once those volumes are set, arrange for the singer to do voice 7. Now, mixing the whole works together, you have *seven* voices on track 3. One voice is first generation, three more voices are second generation, and three voices are third generation. You can continue this process as far as you want, but notice how you've kept the number of generations down and the sound fidelity up.

Most four-channel equipment allows you to record several channels at once and mix them down to a mono channel or OVERDUB them to new stereo channels. For instance, you could make a stereo recording of a guitar and a singer on tracks 1 and 2. You could next make a stereo recording of the singer and a drum on channels 3 and 4. While making that recording, you could be playing the stereo sound from tracks 1 and 2, rerecording them on 3 and 4. Your result would be two singers, a drum, and a guitar all in stereo on tracks 3 and 4. This leaves tracks 1 and 2 empty, ready for more sound to be dubbed onto them.

Another option is to OVERDUB a mono recording of several instruments or singers and place them on one channel. Leave that channel alone while working with the remaining three. By dubbing back and forth on those three channels, you add more instruments or vocals, finally placing this mix on channel 2. You can do the same for channels 3 and 4, finally ending up with a dozen or so musical harmonies on four channels.

You could play back this four-channel music as is or mix it down to stereo (or monaural, if you wish) while copying it onto another tape. This is called a MIXDOWN. In the above case, you could play track 1 of the original four-track tape into the left channel of a normal stereo cassette recorder while playing tracks 2, 3, and 4 into the right channel of your stereo tape deck. Thus you've mixed four into two. Figure 8-5 diagrams the process.

Many decks and mixers have PAN POTS that allow you to send a particular channel or track of sound into the left or right output of the device, thereby sending it to the left or right channel of another recorder. The PAN POT also allows you to send the track just to the left or just to the right, to both channels, or perhaps 25 percent to the left channel and 75 percent to the right channel. The 75 percent/25 percent is the most common case in MIXDOWNS because you seldom want an instrument coming totally from one speaker or the other (if you do, it sounds really strange when people wear headphones and sounds somewhat weird when heard over speakers).

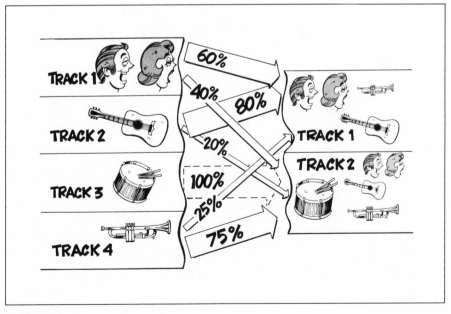

FIGURE 8-5 Mixdown to stereo

Some tape recorders don't have built-in mixers, which means you have to use a separate external mixer to do your overdubbing. Figure 8-6 shows how to connect it. The OVERDUBBING process is about the same as it was before. Play the output of channel 1 into input 1 of the mixer and maybe play a second sound source into channel 2. Maybe you would have a narrator's microphone going into channel 3. The final result would be fed to the tape recorder's channel 2.

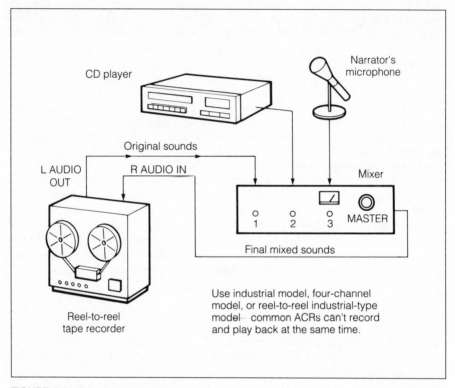

FIGURE 8-6   Overdubbing using a mixer

CHAPTER 9

COMPACT DISC PLAYERS
AND TURNTABLES

Audiomakers *play* a lot of audio, much of which comes from compact discs (CDs) and records. Selecting, caring for, and feeding these little demons is just as important as the virgin sound you create yourself.

CD PLAYERS

Many sound effects and background music come from CDs. They give excellent frequency response (5–20 kHz ±1 dB), dynamite dynamic range (90 dB), superb signal-to-noise ratio (90 dB), heavenly harmonic distortion (less than 0.01 percent), and wonderful wow and flutter (below measurable limits). CDs yield extraordinary fidelity for the price and are quite durable, allowing them to be played thousands of times without deterioration.

Compact discs store the music digitally. When you play a compact disc, a laser beams its light onto a spiral beneath the surface of the disc. The light reflects from this sublayer except where opaque pits are etched. The reflected light is converted into 1's and 0's, which are then converted into an analog audio signal that can be amplified and sent to your speakers.

Although you can copy the music from a compact disc, you can't directly copy the coded 1's and 0's onto a digital audio tape (DAT) and thus make a perfectly flawless copy. DAT uses data at a different speed than CDs. (So much for buying one copy of a CD and "knocking off" one hundred perfect DAT copies for your friends.)

Not all CD players are the same. When buying one, make sure the features (INDEXING, SCAN, PAUSE, CUE, read-out in seconds, REPEAT, etc.) match your needs. Does the *analog* amplifier (the part that sends the music out of the machine *after* it has been converted from 1's and 0's) have good specifications? It is a shame to run stellar sound through a sleazy preamplifier.

Next check the error correction system. Some CD players go to great lengths to catch every error and cover it elegantly. Others cheaply mask the "hole" with low-quality distorted sound. To test a CD player, buy a CD yourself and scuff the disc up with curved scratches (they are harder for the machine to cover up). Listen and compare it with other models.

Make sure that the compact disc you buy isn't warped. Also, be aware that some discs have been digitally recorded in the sound studio while others are simply copies of analog tape recordings. The analog recordings aren't bad per se because excellent studio equipment is usually used. Audio gourmets, however, feel that digital masters are better.

To help you discern the analog-mastered discs from the pure digital recordings, the Society of Professional Audio Recording Studios (SPARS) devised a three-digit code using A's and D's (for analog and digital) to identify a CD's lineage. The first digit identifies the *original* recording as analog or digital; the second position identifies whether the original recording was mixed to either a digital or analog recorder. The third position specifies whether the mixdown was made into a digital or analog recording for conversion to the 44,100-bits-per-second CD laser master. Thus the code *AAD* means the source was recorded on an analog tape, mixed to an analog tape recorder, and then transferred to a digital master.

TURNTABLES

If a $200 CD player is better than a $1,000 phonograph turntable, why bother with records? Reasons:

1. Huge archives of discs have been pressed over the years, records that are too old, too rare, or too esoteric to be converted to CDs. If you want something old or special, it's probably available on a long-playing (LP) record.

2. Music purists believe that an *excellent* turntable with an *excellent* CARTRIDGE and STYLUS playing a well-preserved record sounds *better* than a CD.

Selecting a Turntable

Avoid turntables that change records, play the record sideways, or pop the record out of a drawer. These are built for convenience or show, not sound.

The best turntable is one that rotates the record at a perfectly constant speed yet doesn't rumble or resonate from motor vibration, bearings, or outside noises. Let's examine each part of the turntable system.

The chassis that holds the turntable mechanism should dampen resonances and isolate the PLATTER from outside vibrations (footsteps, motor noise, loudspeaker sound). If you tap the turntable and hear the *twang, twang* of springs, keep your pesos in your pocket and look elsewhere. Try this test: Play a record at normal volume, stop the record (with the needle still in the groove), and listen. You shouldn't hear anything. Tap the turntable frame with your finger; the less sound that emanates from the speaker, the better.

What makes the PLATTER spin is the DRIVE. The cheapest drive is shown in Figure 9-1, the RIM DRIVE. Minor bumps in the IDLER wheel tend to give RIM DRIVE turntables RUMBLE and FLUTTER.

The next best is the DIRECT DRIVE, in which the motor and PLATTER are combined into one mechanical part. The advantage of DIRECT DRIVE is that there are fewer parts to wear out or mess up . . . mess up . . . mess up.

Ardent fidelity fusspots demand BELT DRIVE turntables, which have excellent speed control and low FLUTTER and RUMBLE. BELT DRIVE turntables, however, are hard to cue up because they take a long time to start spinning, whereas RIM DRIVES start up quickly.

The PLATTER should be heavy enough to smooth out minor speed irregularities and to damp out spurious resonances that come from the motor or from outside the turntable. Tap the PLATTER with a sharp object and listen closely; it should make a dull *thunk* rather than a *ting . . . ing* sound.

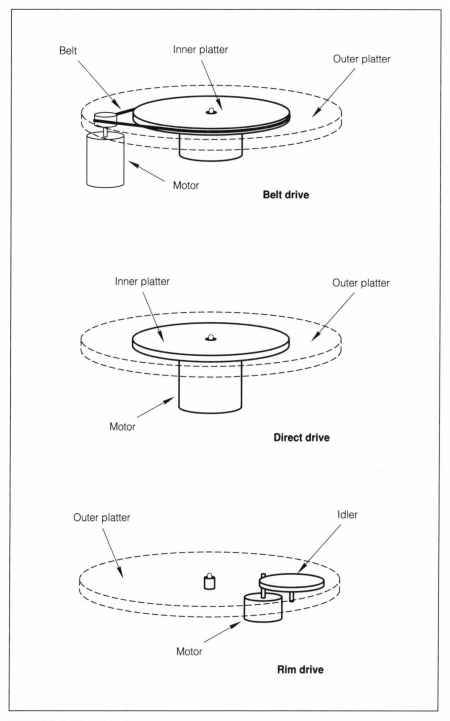

FIGURE 9-1 Turntable drives

The TONE ARM (the part that holds the needle and CARTRIDGE) should also resist resonances. If you tap a good ARM with your fingernail, it should go *thonk*, not *tonngg*. Although the standard PIVOTING TONE ARM is cheap and simple to maintain, the LATERAL TRACKING arm is preferred by some because it allows the needle to follow the groove at a more precise angle.

Selecting Styli and Cartridges

Diamond record needles (STYLI) come in several shapes and qualities—CONICAL, ELLIPTICAL, and LINE CONTACT (Figure 9-2). The CONICAL tip, cheap and common, misses some musical detail and wears the grooves fairly rapidly.

The more expensive ELLIPTICAL STYLUS is sleeker and rides deeper in the groove, catching more of the high frequencies and causing less wear.

True audio devotees buy LINE CONTACT or MICRORIDGE STYLI. They are flatter than their ELLIPTICAL brothers and ride even deeper in the groove, allowing more surface area to contact the groove. This causes less wear and follows the groove more closely (sensing higher frequencies).

The STYLUS sticks into a vibration sensor called a CARTRIDGE, which makes the electrical signal that goes to your amplifier. Kids' turntables and other cheapie models use CERAMIC CARTRIDGES that contain crystals, which when vibrated produce a fairly strong electrical signal.

All other CARTRIDGES are MAGNETIC: a coil of wire and a magnet inside produce the electrical signal from the vibrating stylus. MAGNETIC CARTRIDGES make weak signals, similar to a microphone, and require extra preamplification. The sound fidelity is excellent.

Turntable Setup

Set your turntable on a sturdy (not wobbly, not vibration-prone) table, stand, or shelf away from flexing floors, vibrating speakers, and wind. Using a level, adjust the feet (or spring supports) on your turntable so that the record PLATTER is perfectly level.

Adjust the tone arm's COUNTERBALANCE (the weight of the back of the TONE ARM) so that the needle presses against the record with a 1- to 1.5-gram force. Unless you have a very sensitive fingertip, you will need a TRACKING FORCE GAUGE to make this measurement.

Next, adjust the ANTISCATE FORCE by playing an album with not much music and a wide runout (no grooves at the end). Adjust the ANTISCATE control so that as the smooth, shiny blank part of the record plays, the needle drifts slightly outward.

Replace your STYLUS every few years; replace your CARTRIDGE every five years or so. Good CARTRIDGES cost $50 to $100, but an excellent one—the Joe Grado model MTE+1—runs only $25. Note that not every CARTRIDGE fits every TONE ARM.

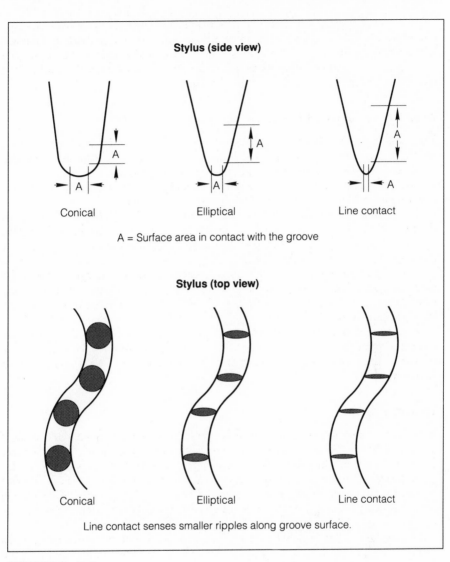

Stylus (side view)

Conical   Elliptical   Line contact

A = Surface area in contact with the groove

Stylus (top view)

Conical   Elliptical   Line contact

Line contact senses smaller ripples along groove surface.

FIGURE 9-2   Styli

SPECIAL AUDIO GIZMOS

You are about to discover that buying your expensive mixer, recorder, amplifier, and speakers was the cheapest part of your hobby.

NOISE REDUCTION SYSTEMS

Noise is anything in the recording that doesn't belong there, such as the sounds of cars on the street and jets flying overhead. Trying to get rid of this noise, we use soundproof rooms and strategically placed directional microphones. Other noises creep into our sound during the recording process. This could be hum or hiss from our wires and circuits. Our biggest enemy is often the hiss from tape. NOISE REDUCTION systems are circuits that endeavor to amplify desired sound while leaving the noise behind.

Dolby and DBX

DOLBY (a trademark of Dolby Laboratories) comes in three versions: DOLBY A, DOLBY B, and DOLBY C. DOLBY A is used by professionals and treats the entire sound spectrum. DOLBY B, used on nearly all inexpensive home audio and video recorders, just works on the high frequencies. DOLBY C is better than B; it works on both the high and midfrequencies. DBX, another NOISE REDUCTION system, gives a more pronounced effect than DOLBY.

All these systems have one thing in common: you must use the process while making your recording (ENCODING) and then use the process again while playing your tape back (DECODING). If you take both steps, then your tape will play back with less noise, especially less hiss.

If you're not going to play your tape back on a DOLBY or DBX machine, don't use the process. Playing an ENCODED tape on a normal machine will produce a shrill, exaggerated sound. DOLBY B, because it is gentler than the other schemes, is a partial exception: if you have to play a DOLBY B tape on a regular machine, it won't sound too bad if you turn the TREBLE or TONE control down on your amplifier.

When playing back normal (nonENCODED) tape, turn your DOLBY or DBX circuits off. They will muffle your sound trying to decode signals that are not there.

Compressors

One problem with recording tape is that loud sounds saturate the tape with magnetism, distorting your sound. Soft sounds, on the other hand, tend to get buried in the hiss. COMPRESSORS solve this problem by altering the dynamics of the sound, making very loud sounds less loud and soft sounds louder. A 4:1 COMPRESSION means that a 4-dB increase in real volume results in a 1-dB increase in signal. This allows the recording engineer to turn up the volume level on his recorder (keeping the soft sounds out of the mud) while the COMPRESSOR keeps the loud sounds from being too loud and saturating the tape.

COMPRESSED sound seems louder to your ear, although it isn't really. Many TV and radio ads are COMPRESSED to cut through traffic noise and household chatter. COMPRESSED sound makes musical pieces easier to hear, especially when you are driving in a car. Eventually the constant blare becomes fatiguing. To correct everything back, the sound needs to be deemphasized by sending it through an EXPANDER.

Expanders

EXPANDERS—the opposite of COMPRESSORS—make loud sounds louder, soft sounds softer, and are good for converting COMPRESSED sound back into normal-sounding sound.

COMPRESSORS and EXPANDERS often are used together: the COMPRESSOR reduces the dynamic range of live music (90 dB) down to what your audiotape recorder can handle (maybe 50 dB). When you play the tape back, you would expand the sound back from 50 dB up to 90 dB.

COMPRESSORS and EXPANDERS aren't necessary for CD, DAT, and hi-fi VCRs—these machines already have a wide dynamic range.

Equalizers

EQUALIZERS selectively adjust frequency response. A bass/treble control or tone control is the most common EQUALIZER. An EQUALIZER boosts some frequencies or cuts others trying to make up for sounds that are too shrill or too bassy.

Filters

FILTERS generally remove one frequency from the sound spectrum. LO-CUT or HI-PASS filters remove low sounds like air conditioning rumble, wind, and microphone-handling noises. LO-PASS or HI-CUT FILTERS remove high tones like scratches on records, hiss, and sibilant spoken s's.

Graphic Equalizers

A GRAPHIC EQUALIZER divides the sound spectrum into anywhere from six to twelve frequency ranges. Sliding the controls on the GRAPHIC EQUALIZER boosts or diminishes *one particular tone*. Hum from a poorly grounded system can be diminished by filtering out the 60-Hz frequency. The rumble of wind can be diminished by filtering out the 30-Hz frequency. The high-pitched whine of an electric motor may require the removal of the 10,000-Hz frequency, while a dusty record may need removal of the 15,000-Hz frequency. If you teamed up several sliders together to pass only the frequencies between 500 Hz and 2500 Hz, your music and speech would sound like it was coming over a telephone. By selectively cutting out or boosting various frequencies, you can deemphasize or emphasize a singer or a particular instrument heard in the orchestra.

Parametric Equalizers

A PARAMETRIC EQUALIZER is an adjustable FILTER. You can tune it to a particular frequency and then turn another knob to cut or boost that frequency. This gadget is usually built into the larger mixers (and is covered further in Chapter 5).

SPECIAL EFFECTS PROCESSORS

SPECIAL EFFECTS PROCESSORS are gizmos that allow you to create sounds that were never there to start with. HARMONIZERS, for instance, take the tone you put into them and synthesize another tone higher or lower, perhaps harmonizing with the original tone. HARMONIZERS are good for creating special effects from singing or synthesizers.

Another special effects device is the TIME COMPRESSOR. It has nothing to do with Star Trek or a sci-fi story by Jules Verne. A TIME COMPRESSOR will take the sounds that come into it and change their pitch up or down. How does it compress time? If you were to play an audiotape faster, the program (musical selection or commercial) would finish more quickly. The pitch, however, would be higher and might sound a little like Donald Duck. Running this same signal through a TIME COMPRESSOR lowers the pitch of the sound so that the words or music come out faster without a pitch shift. The TIME COMPRESSOR is especially handy for shortening or lengthening audio passages so that they fit in a convenient length such as twenty-five seconds for a commercial or thirty minutes for a musical piece that has to fit on a C-60 cassette. TIME COMPRESSORS are often used on television to disguise voices.

Another gizmo, the FLANGER, creates a swooshy, spacy effect, much like what you would get if you listened to an orchestra through a short pipe while swiveling in a chair. FLANGERS are popular among rock bands trying to add pizzazz and dimension to their guitars and synthesizers.

Because the digital circuits are similar for the above three devices, they are generally built into one box that does three jobs. The box may also give you ECHO, REVERBERATION, and DELAY.

Reverberation

Have you ever noticed how singing in the shower makes you sound better? It is due to REVERBERATION, the continuous reflection of sound off the walls back to your ears. You hear almost no REVERBERATION outdoors and little more in a carpeted room with curtains. REVERBERATION increases when you enter a bare room or a cave or a huge metal tank (when is the last time you crawled into a tank?).

REVERBERATION adds space, warmth, and natural ambience to the sound. REVERBERATION also adds depth to a sound effect, making a room or action sound larger.

REVERBERATION and ECHOES are undesirable when you are making recordings, so we work hard to keep microphones close enough to performers to ward off REVERBERATION and maintain clear speech. Once ECHOES and REVERBERATION are part of your sound, you can't get rid of them. If, however, you record your sound without these artifacts, you can use a REVERB to add this natural sound back in.

Adding too much REVERBERATION is the first inclination of an amateur. The sound is so full and rich, it is hard to avoid using it. Generally if you can hear the ambience that you have added to the sound, then you've put in too much. REVERBERATION should be delicate and light. It should never be noticeable like the heavy-duty REVERB of a DJ's voice on a rock radio station.

Inexpensive REVERB units (under $100) add extra sound to a room or a stagelike sound to a teen-ager's electric guitar. For serious audio work, however, high-quality circuits are needed to reproduce a truer fidelity to the original sound. When selecting a REVERB unit, listen carefully to see if it sounds electronic rather than real.

Echo and Delay

DIGITAL DELAY LINES and ECHO CHAMBERS produce effects that are often mistaken for REVERBERATION. The ECHO effect is the repetition one or more times of a sound in its entirety. It is the sound that you hear at the edge of a canyon when you holler "hello . . . hello . . . ello . . . lo," whereas REVERBERATION is the sound that you get when you holler into a steel drum or sing in the bath. Your tones come back to you but you can't tell what the words were.

ECHO CHAMBERS take a simple tune and make it sound complex. When teamed up with a guitar or synthesizer, it sounds like a lot more fingers on the strings and keys.

ECHO CHAMBERS costing under $100 are okay for small bands and tinkerers but don't give the fidelity necessary for professional work. You will probably end up spending $500 for a good ECHO device.

DIGITAL DELAY LINES store up a sound for a moment and then spit it out once, unlike ECHO CHAMBERS, which repeat the sound several times. Use them to double a voice or music, which will create a fuller, richer sound and make it sound like two singers when there's only one or like a small orchestra when there are only three players.

SAMPLERS

A SAMPLER digitally stores a sound and allows you to play it back. For instance, say the word *fussbudget* while pressing the RECORD button on the SAMPLER. When you press the PLAY button, out comes *fussbudget*. Some synthesizer keyboards have SAMPLERS built into them. By pressing the middle C note, the word *fussbudget* comes out as if you had recorded it and played it back. If you now press the next higher note, *fussbudget* will be slightly higher in pitch. You can play a tune with these notes like the cat food commercial that went "meow, meow, meow, meow, meow, meow, meow, meow" in a tune.

As you might expect, the SAMPLER in a $150 synthesizer will not play back with the same fidelity as a $500 SAMPLER. The more professional SAMPLERS are stand-alone units connected to separate keyboards.

AUDIO PATCH BAY

Figure 10-1 shows an AUDIO PATCH BAY, which, like a telephone operator's switchboard, allows any machine to converse with any other machine. Without a PATCH BAY, for the CD player to feed its signal to where the audiocassette player now goes, you'd have to dig around the spaghetti of wires behind the equipment. If the CD player had a plug different from the audiocassette player's, you'd have to find an adapter to make the plug fit the socket. You may even have to remove the equipment from its shelves just

FIGURE 10-1
Audio patch bay

to *see* the plugs. And if you haven't labeled your wires, you'll end up unthreading a tangle of wires that would dumbfound a fisherman.

The solution is to send *all* the inputs and outputs to a PATCH BAY. Here, like the telephone operator, you can externally connect any device to any other device, simply and with a standardized plug.

If you don't want to buy a professional model (about $500), you can make your own AUDIO PATCH BAY using 1/4-inch phone sockets and a plate of metal with holes in it.

Professional PATCH BAYS are often NORMAL-THROUGH or SELF-NORMALLING, which means that if you don't plug anything into the PATCH BAY, whatever is available at the top socket automatically goes to the socket below it. Thus you don't need a messy tangle of wires in your PATCH BAY to make your signals go to the places where they are most likely to be used. As soon as you plug a PATCH CORD into *either* of the top or bottom sockets, the connection is undone and the signal goes wherever the PATCH CORD goes.

BULK TAPE ERASER

A BULK TAPE ERASER is a black box that creates a powerful magnetic field to erase magnetic recordings. It is useful for quickly clearing material off tapes without bothering to run them through recorders (which automatically erase as they record). They *are* very handy when you have used a tape from beginning to end and now wish to put a new program on the first half of the tape. When your new program finishes, you don't want your audience to hear the leftover half of the old program. (Imagine your boss and stockholders catching remnants of *Truly Tasteless Jokes* that didn't get erased from last New Year's party.) The BULK TAPE ERASER erases the entire tape clean so that you may now trust it. BULK ERASERS *cannot* erase *part* of a tape. They erase the *whole reel or cassette* at once.

Small $15 BULK TAPE ERASERS with permanent magnets in them are good for erasing audiocassettes. Much larger ones (about $100) can erase videocassettes (which are much thicker) and audiocassettes with chrome tape (they are harder to erase). A $20 BULK ERASER will demagnetize common audiocassettes and reel-to-reel tapes. Figure 10-2 shows one.

To use an electric BULK TAPE ERASER,

1. Place the BULK ERASER and the tape to be erased at least 6 feet away from your other tapes so they don't get slightly erased by stray magnetic fields.

FIGURE 10-2
Bulk tape eraser

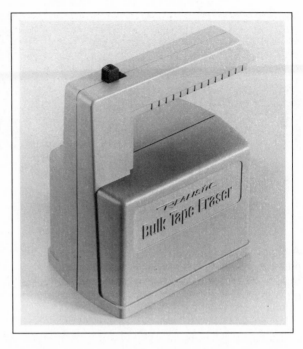

2. Place the tape on the ERASER, press the ON button, and hold it down.

3. Rotate the tape a few times so that all of the reel or cassette passes over or under the device.

4. To be thorough, turn the cassette or reel over and repeat the process on the other side.

5. *With the button still held down,* lift the tape from the ERASER (or vice versa), hold it out to arm's length, and then let up on the button.

You hold the tape away from the ERASER when you let up on the button because when you turn the ERASER off it creates a surge of magnetism that leaves a small signal on the tape. Holding the tape away keeps this small pulse from being recorded on the tape.

One little caution about using a BULK TAPE ERASER. If you wear an electric watch, take it off. The powerful magnetic field may scramble your circuits (this could get you ticked off!).

AUDIO MAINTENANCE

Audio circuits generally don't go bad; it's the moving mechanical parts—switches, plugs, motors, wheels, speakers, push buttons, and relays—that cause most of the trouble. And, as they used to say in driving school, there's always a problem with the nut behind the wheel.

CLEANING AUDIO HEADS

When tape moves over the audio record/playback heads in your cassette or reel-to-reel tape recorder, it can carry with it dirt and flaking oxide, which builds up and creates a gap between the head and the tape. This tiny deviation causes a muffled sound to be recorded or played back from the tape.

When to Clean the Heads

1. The sound becomes weak, garbled, or muffled
2. The highs are suddenly missing from a good tape
3. Once an hour if you are using flaky, wrinkled, old, or cheap tape
4. Once every couple hours if you do a lot of editing
5. Once every couple weeks if your recorder is in a clean, climate-controlled studio with a cover over the machine between uses
6. The tape squeaks or sticks as it passes through the machine

If numerous cleanings don't improve the situation, maybe your heads have been knocked out of alignment or are worn-out. (They generally last 2,000 to 3,000 hours.) As they wear, they lose their high-frequency response, muffling the sound.

If your tape deck eats tapes, your CAPSTAN or PINCH ROLLER may be dirty (sticky), warranting a scrubdown.

What to Use

You don't use Head and Shoulders and a scrub brush to clean audio heads. You have two choices for cleaning the heads and tape path:

1. A tape head-cleaning cassette
2. Manually cleaning the heads and path with a swab and solvent

Number 1 is the easiest but ineffective against really tough dirt. Number 2— thorough and effective against sticky dirt—is best if you are handy with a screwdriver (or a vodka collins) and a swab.

Cassette Head Cleaners Cassette head cleaners are a necessity for cleaning car cassette players and other hard-to-reach cassette players. Nobody wants to take their car dashboard apart to clean the heads on their tape player.

Figure 11-1 shows two common types of cassette head cleaners—a *dry type* and a *wet type*. The dry type is less expensive, but I prefer the wet type, which comes with a bottle of cleaning fluid that you use to wet a cloth ribbon in the cassette or to wet felt pads that rub against the head, capstan, and pinch roller.

Make sure that all of the wet places have dried before reinserting a new audiocassette into the machine; you don't want any remaining drips to dissolve the recording on your audiocassette.

Cassette Cleaning Kits For the more adventuresome among you, there are manual head-cleaning kits (Figure 11-2) containing swabs and a bottle of juice. You can also buy head-cleaner spray, but don't try to spray it into your machine. Spray the cleaner on a swab and then wipe the swab across the tape heads.

Instead of using prepared liquids and special swabs, you can save a few bucks by buying cotton swabs such as Q-Tips and ethyl alcohol from your drugstore.

How to Do It

If you buy a cassette-cleaning kit, you will get instructions with the kit. If you're cleaning the tape mechanism manually yourself, here's how the process would generally go:

Reel-to-reel Recorders   To clean the tape path and heads,

1. Remove the tape from the machine.
2. Check to see if the heads have a removable head cover that can be pulled out of the way. These covers either snap off, pull straight up and off, or require removal

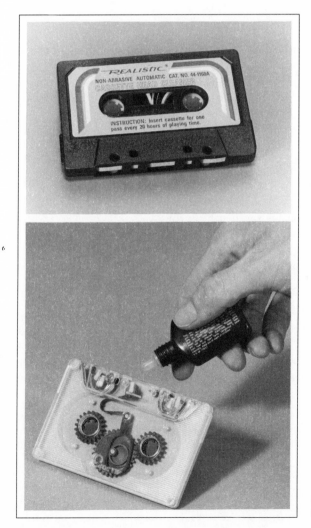

FIGURE 11-1
Cassette head cleaners

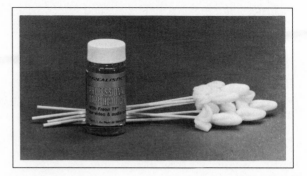

of a screw. On some machines you can see the heads and don't need to remove the head cover.

3. Using a flashlight, take a look; if you see lots of brown dust, blow it or vacuum it out.

4. Dip your swab in the cleaning fluid and rub it across the large, shiny playback head.

5. If your swab isn't dirty, then dip it again and shoot for the record head, which is probably upstream of the playback head. Some machines combine the two heads into a single record/playback head.

6. If your swab still looks clean then shoot for the silvery capstan that drives the tape through the machine. Wipe it on all sides.

The parts you just cleaned are the most dirt-sensitive. By cleaning them first, your swab stayed fairly clean. Next we go to the less critical parts, which will make your swab dirty fast.

7. Find the erase head—probably the first head the tape meets as it enters the machine—and wipe the face of the head.

8. Now wipe all of the tape guides—the little posts or wheels over which the tape slides or rolls while it is passing through the machine.

9. Now clean the pinch roller—the large round rubber roller next to the capstan. You can rotate the roller with your finger along the top edge while pressing the swab against the face of the roller. Try not to leave fingerprints on the face of the roller. The rubber roller dissolves easily so your swab will get dirty quickly. Don't worry about it; turn the swab over and keep wiping for a couple of revolutions around the roller.

10. Now let everything dry before reassembling the head covers and putting tape in the machine.

Cassette Recorders   Cleaning cassette recorders is difficult because it is so hard to get in where the heads are hiding. Professional cassette recorders have removable head covers (just like reel-to-reel tape recorders) that snap off, pull off, or come off after removing a screw.

On a common tape recorder, pop open the cassette door by pressing EJECT. After removing any cassette, see if you can reach the heads and tape guides. Some tape machines have cassette lids that can be opened further than normal just by pulling on them. In other words, they pop open a little ways for insertion of tapes, but can be pulled open further for head cleaning. Don't pull too hard just in case your cassette is *not* one of those that opens further (or else you'll make it real easy to clean forevermore).

Some cassette lids have easy-to-reach screws or clips that allow you to remove the cassette lid, revealing the mechanism inside. Some cassette players have a little floor that lifts the cassette up when it is ejected; this floor is sometimes in the way and needs to be pushed back down to reveal the heads.

Once you can see the inside of the mechanism, follow essentially the same steps as you would for a reel-to-reel tape recorder.

DEMAGNETIZING TAPE HEADS

While you are cleaning the heads, it's a good time to DEMAGNETIZE (DEGAUSS) them as well.

Audiotape heads are electromagnets that are magnetized by oscillating electrical currents. When the current stops, the heads should become nonmagnetic. Sometimes, however, long usage or very loud recording signals can cause a small amount of residual magnetism to remain. This can gradually erase your tapes every time they play over the head. You might not notice the effect at first, but you will begin to lose high-frequency response and gain tape hiss.

Avoid this problem by periodically DEMAGNETIZING your tape heads, maybe every time you clean them. Both steps should be done before you commence an expensive or important recording or editing session.

To DEMAGNETIZE audio heads, use an electrical tool called a HEAD DEMAGNETIZER or HEAD DEGAUSSER (shown in Figure 11-3). Here's how to use it:

1. Turn off the tape recorder.

2. Remove the tape so that *it* doesn't get demagnetized (erased) by the HEAD DEMAGNETIZER.

3. Turn on the HEAD DEMAGNETIZER, often by plugging it in. Other models have an on/off switch; fancy ones even have a light. Bring the probe very close to the audio playback head. If the probe has a rubber cover to keep it from scratching the head, you may even touch the probe against the head. Hold it there about a second and then *slowly* move it to the next head, perhaps the record or erase head. *Slowly* move it from head to head, from tape guide to tape guide, and then to the capstan.

4. When finished, withdraw the probe *very slowly*.

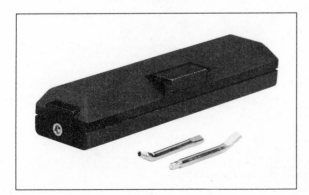

FIGURE 11-3
Tape head demagnetizer

5. Hold the probe a foot or two away from the mechanism before shutting it off because when you shut it off, it sends out a little pulse of magnetism. Your object is to DEMAGNETIZE the heads, so you don't want that magnetic pulse to be left on the heads.

SLIPPERY BELTS AND WHEELS

Some record players and tape recorders are DIRECT DRIVE, meaning that the motor directly drives the capstan or turntable. There are no belts or pulleys or little rubber wheels to slip or wear out. For this reason DIRECT DRIVE devices have fewer maintenance problems than their belt- and pulley-driven brothers.

Many other audio devices use belts and clutches to make things go around. One motor drives everything. When the belts get old, stretched, or slippery, the part that is supposed to go around slips too, reducing its speed or making its speed uneven. If your tape recorder plays music at a slightly slower speed than it used to, if its wind or rewind is very slow, or if there is a lot of wow and flutter in music (especially noticeable in piano music), you may have a slippery capstan or a slippery or stretched belt that drives the capstan.

Open the machine and examine the belt. If it feels loose or looks stretched, replace the belt. If the belt appears shiny, it could be glazed. Apply a nonslip solvent like the one in Figure 11-4 that can clean glazed belts and slippery pulleys, making them grab better.

The same problem happens with turntables. If your rock and roll drags like a fugue, if your piano rhapsodies have a warbling sound, if gently touching the turntable turns polkas into waltzes, or if your automatic turntable seems to bog down when changing records, the IDLER wheel or drive belts are probably glazed or tired.

FIGURE 11-4
Nonslip solvent for belts
and idler wheels

LP RECORD AND CD CARE

LP Records

LP records are very delicate, and if you don't take good care of them, they'll snap and pop at you. Some hints:

1. Keep your records meticulously clean by
   a. Keeping the turntable's platter clean.
   b. Sweeping the record in the direction of the grooves with a fiber brush or velvet pad *each* time you play it.
   c. Handling record discs by their edges and label.
   d. When a record gets dirty, washing it with a record cleaner like Triton X-114 from Rohm-Haas or Monolan 2000 from Diamond Shamrock.
2. Store records with care by
   a. Storing albums vertically, close together, but not squashed like sardines.
   b. Storing records away from sun and heat.
   c. Storing records in their paper sleeves or, better yet, in polyethylene sleeves or rice paper sleeves. Don't just stuff the record in the cardboard jacket; there's too much lint in there.
   d. Discarding the shrinkwrap that covers the album cover. Its static electricity attracts dust, and the wrap sometimes becomes too tight, warping the record.

CDs

Regardless of what you have heard, you cannot use CDs as frisbees or coasters, even though they will play if scratched and smeared with fingerprints. Error correction circuitry in CD players covers up momentary lapses in signal (some models do this better than others), but you never get something for nothing. Covered-up sound is not *true* sound. The compensation process adds fakery and distortion to the sound. Really bad scratches and dirt will overload even the best error correction circuits, causing your CD to skip, mute, jump ahead, or even eject. To protect your CDs,

1. Keep them in their "jewel cases" (except when playing them, of course).
2. Handle the discs by the rims only.
3. Clean CDs gently with a soft lint-free cloth, radially from the center to the edge like the spokes of a wheel, not in the direction of rotation.

TAPE CARE

Most audio productions are stored on tape, which is a plastic ribbon covered with a magnetic powder. Anything that nicks, wrinkles, or scrapes the magnetic powder off the film is bad news.

Tapes' two worst enemies are *heat* and *dirt*. Hot radiators, hot cars, sunny windowsills, dusty workshops, and sandy, salty beaches can wreck an audiocassette. Store your cassettes in their plastic cases and keep reel-to-reel tapes in their boxes when not in use. Never, never, never leave an audiocassette sitting on the dashboard of your car on a hot sunny day; it will shrivel up like bacon.

Tapes can easily last for fifty years if you treat them as follows:

1. Store tape reels upright like books on a bookshelf.
2. Keep cassettes and reels of tape in their boxes. This keeps out dust and dirt.
3. Store tapes at average temperature and humidity—about 70° F (20° C) and 50 percent or less humidity.
4. Keep tapes away from magnetic fields such as hi-fi speakers, amplifiers, transformers, magnets, or big electric motors. Don't store tapes on the top of your TV set because your color TV has a demagnetizer built into its screen.
5. Remove the SAFETY TAB on any cassette that you wish to make erase-proof.

COMMON AUDIO AILMENTS AND CURES

Figure 11-5 shows how several audio signals progress through a mixer and how to troubleshoot a problem. Sound can be ruined at its source, in the cables, in the mixer, in the mixer's cables, at the recorder, and in the cables from the recorder to its monitor or speakers.

I generally plug my headphones into the last machine in the audio chain, usually the tape recorder that is recording my program. If anything is wrong along the way, I will hear the problem from the recorder. If I don't get sound, I start working my way back toward the source. Here are some specific problems and solutions in detail.

1. *If the microphone sound is weak, tinny, or has hum or hiss,*
   a. The mike is not right for your recorder. Read Chapter 2 about impedance, balanced lines, and adapters.
   b. The mike may be defective or of poor quality.
   c. The connection may be bad or you may be using the wrong kind of mike wire.
   d. In an electret condenser mike, the battery may be weak.
2. *If the sound played from another device distorts, is raspy, or has a lot of hum and hiss, the audio signal may be too strong.*
   a. Reduce the volume from the source.
   b. Attenuate the signal using a PAD.
   c. If using your recorder's MIC IN, switch to an AUX IN, AUDIO IN, or LINE IN that can accept a more powerful signal.
3. *If while playing a video tape, you get no sound, the wrong sound, two sound tracks at once, or what seems like half the sound,*
   a. Video tapes can have two sound tracks. You can listen to channel 1, 2, or a mixture of both. The trick is to play back the correct one. If you hear no sound, perhaps you are listening to the silent track; try the other. If you hear Spanish and you want English, perhaps the tape is bilingual and you are listening to the wrong track; try the other. If you hear both languages together, perhaps your AUDIO SELECT switch is on MIX; switch it to channel 1 or channel 2. If you are running an audio cable from the channel 1 AUDIO OUT to a separate amplifier and loudspeaker, then channel 1 will be all the amplifier hears, no matter where you throw the AUDIO SELECT switch. You have to unplug the cable

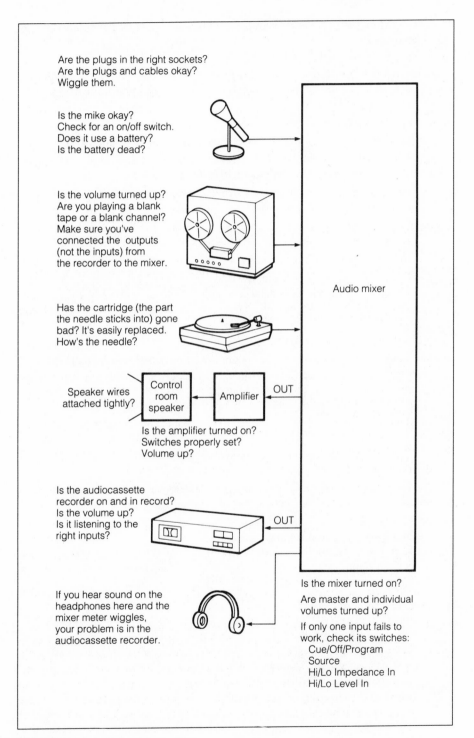

Are the plugs in the right sockets?
Are the plugs and cables okay?
Wiggle them.

Is the mike okay?
Check for an on/off switch.
Does it use a battery?
Is the battery dead?

Is the volume turned up?
Are you playing a blank
tape or a blank channel?
Make sure you've
connected the outputs
(not the inputs) from
the recorder to the mixer.

Audio mixer

Has the cartridge (the part
the needle sticks into) gone
bad? It's easily replaced.
How's the needle?

Speaker wires
attached tightly?

Control
room
speaker

Amplifier   OUT

Is the amplifier turned on?
Switches properly set?
Volume up?

Is the audiocassette
recorder on and in record?
Is the volume up?
Is it listening to the
right inputs?

OUT

Is the mixer turned on?

Are master and individual
volumes turned up?

If you hear sound on the
headphones here and the
mixer meter wiggles,
your problem is in the
audiocassette recorder.

If only one input fails to
work, check its switches:
  Cue/Off/Program
  Source
  Hi/Lo Impedance In
  Hi/Lo Level In

FIGURE 11-5 Audio troubleshooting

from the channel 1 output and stick it into the channel 2 socket to hear channel 2.

b. Hi-fi VCRs record their hi-fi sound as part of the picture. If you dub in new sound, this gets recorded in the linear (non-hi-fi) audio tracks. When playing back such a tape, switch the machine to the low-fidelity linear tracks to hear your newly dubbed sound.

4. *If the mixer passes a signal from all but one microphone,*

a. The problem is in that microphone, cable, plug, or mixer input. Does the mike have an on/off switch that is off?

b. Is it an ELECTRET CONDENSOR mike with a dead battery?

c. Try wiggling the wire near the mike and near the plug to see if the sound crackles. If it does, you may have a loose, broken, or frayed wire.

d. Sometimes you hear a lot of hum when a wire breaks. Check for a broken wire on some plugs by unscrewing the plug handle and looking at the wire.

e. Are the mixer's switches properly set?

f. Does the mixer's IMPEDANCE match that of the mike? Try another mike in the same input; if the problem persists, check the mixer once again because that mixer input is probably at fault. If the problem stops, the first mike or its cable is defective.

5. *If all audio from the mixer has hum,*

a. Ground the mixer to the amplifier and to the sources. One way to do this is to plug them all into the same multiple AC outlet so the grounding wires in the electric cords all are going to the same place. Another solution is to attach a bare wire to the chassis of each device, stringing them all together.

b. Make sure that the source volume, mixer volume, and recorder volume are all sharing the load. One should not be way up while another is way down.

c. Check for a broken ground or shield wire from the mixer to the amplifier or recorder.

6. *If the sound is good except when you hear radio stations, police calls, CB radios, the buzz of fluorescent lamps, or the tick, tick, tick of automobile ignitions in the background of your recording,*

Presumably you couldn't hear these sounds with your unaided ears, but you could through the audio devices. These signals are electromagnetic radiation inducing a signal in your wire. In a way it's as if your wires were acting like an antenna picking up these signals.

a. Try to keep away from the interference sources.

b. Ensure that you have good shielding in your source cables and the cables from the mixer to the recorder.

c. Run the mixer's HI-LEVEL OUT to the LINE IN of the recorder rather than using the MIC-LEVEL OUT and the recorder's MIC IN, if you can. By using the stronger signals, the interference will seem weak in comparison.

d. Use balanced lines whenever possible.

e. Ground the devices together with a wire connecting their chassis.

    f. Use short cables whenever possible.

    g. Contact the local Federal Communications Commission (FCC) if you think someone might be broadcasting with too much power. Some CB radios may be souped up or poorly grounded, sending renegade signals everywhere.

7. *If your turntable or record player sounds unusually scratchy and the needle skips,*

    a. Needles wear out and so do records. How long has this machine been in use?

    b. Diamond needles, especially if heavily used, sometimes chip, leaving a stub that will stay in the groove but won't play very well. Try changing the needle. Many turntable needles can simply be pulled out and a new one stuffed into the cartridge.

    c. Your platter isn't level. Use a bubble-type level to set it straight.

    d. Your tracking force may be too low. Increase it, using a stylus pressure gauge to reset the tracking weight to manufacturer's specifications.

    e. Your antiscate control may be set too high.

8. *If your turntable has faint hum or buzz in the background,*

    a. The turntable's grounding wire has come loose. Check it both at the rear of the table and at its destination, usually the back of the preamplifier mixer or amplifier/receiver.

    b. Check the cartridge leads for tightness.

    c. Try reversing the turntable's power line cord.

    d. Make sure your turntable isn't too close to the preamplifier, amplifier, high-intensity lamp, motors, or other devices that radiate AC magnetism. The same is true for your cables and preamplifier.

9. *If your turntable has a boomy sound or rumble,*

    a. Move it farther from the speakers.

    b. Place it on a more solid support.

    c. Lubricate the spindle bearing with black Linn or Merrill oil.

10. *If you hear a faint buzz in the background of your sound, but the buzz isn't always there,*

    Hairdryers, shavers, blowers, air conditioners, other motors, light dimmers, three-way lamps, some fluorescent fixtures, and computers all radiate electrical interference, which can radiate through the air or pass through the electrical wiring and into your amplifiers, mixers, or musical instruments.

    a. Try to find the offending device and turn it off. If the buzzing is driving you crazy, go to your circuit breaker panel and turn off everything in the house *except* your audio system. Is the noise gone? If no, the problem is probably not in your house. If yes, then switch the breakers on, one by one, until the noise comes back. Now that you have narrowed down the circuit, unplug everything on that circuit and add them back one by one until the buzz returns. The culprit can now be unplugged while you are recording.

    b. Buy and install an AC LINE NOISE FILTER like the one in Figure 11-6. This device absorbs electrical interference from motors and so forth before these signals can travel down your power line and get into your sound recordings. For best results, plug the offending device, which you found in step (*a*) above, into

FIGURE 11-6
AC line noise or
interference filter

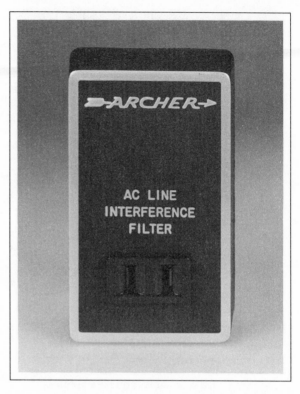

the FILTER. Another solution, though less effective, is to plug your audio equipment into a FILTER. If you have several offending motors or several audio
devices, you may need to buy several FILTERS.

  c. Some inexpensive lamp dimmers put out a buzzing sound called radio
frequency interference (RFI). Replace these dimmers with more expensive
ones that have RFI suppression (a feature usually listed on the box). Incidentally, turning your dimmer all the way on or off will probably reduce the
interference.

11. *If sound crackles, cuts out, or pops in and out, you have a dirty or corroded connection.*

  a. Find the offender by wiggling or twisting plugs (except multipin ones—these
you unplug and reinsert) until you restore the sound. Often you can polish a
corroded plug or socket with a pencil eraser or fine sandpaper.

  b. Flip back and forth a half dozen times any switches that affect the sound. The
contacts on slide switches sometimes get corroded.

  c. Rotate your volume or tone controls up and down a few times. The sliders
inside can get dirty and start to crackle.

  d. If a few flips of the switches or rotations of the volume controls don't clear up
the problem, buy some CONTACT CLEANER and spray it into the errant switch or
potentiometer body. The spray comes with a tiny straw that can be inserted
into an opening in the switch or volume control assembly so you can spritz

some of the juice onto the contacts. Then flip the switch a dozen times or so or rotate the knob to clean the surface.

12. *If your speakers sizzle, buzz, or rattle,*

If you hear a hum or hiss when there's *no* music playing, the problem is not in your speaker, for speakers don't *make* sound, they reproduce it; check your amplifier, preamplifier, mixer, or source. If you hear a problem when playing music,

a. Remove the grille cloth and tighten the screws that hold the drivers to the cabinet. The screws loosen with time.

b. Is the wood coming apart or delaminating? Is the grille cover loose?

c. Gently and evenly push the MIDRANGE and WOOFER cones in. They should move freely without scraping. If they scrape, your speaker may be warped and due for replacement.

d. Swap the left speaker wires with the right speaker wires. If the problem is suddenly in the other speaker, the problem is in your source, mixer, cables, or amplifier, not the speaker. If you hear sizzling in both speakers, it's probably an amplifier or mixer problem as seldom do two speakers fail simultaneously.

e. Check shelves, wall hangings, and paneling; they may be sizzling, not your speakers. Try swapping your speakers. If the sizzle remains in the same place, it's your house, not your speaker, that's chattering at you.

13. *If your speaker lacks highs, lows, or midranges,*

a. You may have blown a WOOFER, MIDRANGE, or TWEETER. Cover two with pillows and see if the remaining driver makes any sound.

14. *If you hear hum,*

a. Turn down the amplifier volume. If the speakers still hum, you have a problem in the amplifier that requires grounding or technical help.

b. If the hum is heard only with the amplifier turned up, then it's the preamplifier, mixer, or cables. Disconnect each to see if the hum stops.

c. Disconnect a particular source if the hum comes from it. If the hum doesn't stop, the problem is downstream, in the mixer perhaps. If the hum does stop, make a better ground from the source to the mixer. Try turning the AC plug over.

d. Turn down the source's volume control. If the hum goes away, the noise is indeed generated by the source. If it remains, the hum is most likely in the cables to the mixer or preamplifier; check for broken ground wires.

15. *If your audiocassette player eats tapes,*

a. Clean the capstan and pinch roller; they're dirty or sticky.

b. Your audiocassette may be warped and jamming the recorder (not the recorder's fault). Discard the cassette.

16. *If your CD player skips easily,*

a. Move the player farther from your speakers. The speaker sound is vibrating your disc as it plays, and the laser beam can't follow the moving target.

b. Clean the laser (see manufacturer's instructions). It may be smudged or dusty.

G L O S S A R Y

AC   Alternating current: power you get from a wall outlet in your home.

AGC   *See* Automatic volume (gain) control.

Analog   The converse of digital in that a signal may have an infinite number of gradations. Analog recordings store the waves of the original signal as similar waves in the recorded medium.

Antifeedback control   Audio filter on a public address amplifier to cut out resonant unwanted frequencies and to reduce feedback.

Antiscate   Turntable mechanism that impedes the tone arm's natural tendency to slide toward the center of the record.

Attenuator   Small electronic device—sometimes built into an adapter—that decreases the strength of an audio signal. *See also* Pad.

Audio amplifier   Electronic device that strengthens an audio signal, often taking a low-level or high-level signal and making it a speaker-level signal.

Audio attenuator   Device that connects a high-level audio source and a low-level input to reduce the signal strength.

Audio dub   Replaces the sound track on a video recording with new sound

Audio playback head   Tiny electromagnet able to convert magnetic vibrations (recorded on tape) into electrical vibrations that can then be amplified and sent to a speaker.

Audio record head   Block of metal with an electromagnet inside that converts an electrical audio signal into magnetic vibrations that can be recorded onto a tape sliding over the head.

Audition   *See* Cue.

Automatic gain control   *See* Automatic volume control.

Automatic volume control (AVC) or automatic gain control (AGC)   A circuit in an audio device that automatically, electronically senses the volume level and adjusts it up or down to ensure a proper recording.

Aux level input   Input that takes high-level signals.

Aux receive   Input on a mixer that accepts sound from an external audio processor or a special effects device such as an echo chamber.

AVC   *See* Automatic volume control

Balanced lines   Professional-type audio cables with two wires inside a shield. Uses a three-prong plug.

Bass port   A specially tuned opening in a speaker enclosure that allows the bass tones to resonate and escape with more strength.

Bass roll-off   Mike or mixer switch that decreases the bass (low-frequency) signals.

Belt drive   Preferred method of spinning a turntable platter, using a belt wrapped around the platter and the motor shaft.

Bias   Audiotape recorder circuit that matches the recorder's circuits to the kind of tape being used.

Boom   An arm at the top of a mike stand that holds the mike farther from the stand.

Boundary effect   A funneling of sound by a flat surface: a mike placed on the surface clearly picks up the sounds of anyone speaking above the surface. Phenomenon used by pressure-zone microphones.

Bulk tape eraser   Device that demagnetizes and erases an entire tape at once.

Cable tie   Small plastic strap that neatly bundles wires together.

Canon connector   *See* XLR.

Capstan   Spinning shaft in a recorder that pulls the tape through the machine at an even speed.

Cardioid microphone   Microphone with a heart-shaped polar pattern; more sensitive in front of it than to the sides.

Cartridge   Vibration sensor that turns the needle's oscillations into an electrical signal in a turntable.

Cassette shell   The package that holds the audiocassette tape.

CD   *See* Compact disc.

Center channel   An acoustical phenomenon whereby stereo speakers create the image of sound coming from a space between them.

Ceramic cartridge   Phonograph cartridge that uses a piezoelectric crystal to convert record needle vibrations into electric vibrations.

Channel   An individual audio circuit in an amplifier or recorder. A monaural device has one channel; a stereo device has two channels, left (L) and right (R).

Channel separation   *See* Cross talk; Separation.

Chrome tape   Medium-high-fidelity audiotape made of chromium dioxide. Use the high-bias setting on your ACR when using this tape.

Compact disc   A 4-3/4-inch digitally recorded silvery disc that can hold up to seventy-five minutes of sound, played back by the reflected light of a laser beam in a compact disc player.

Compressor   Audio device that reduces the dynamic range (loudness) of louder sounds without affecting softer sounds.

Conical stylus   Inexpensive round-shaped turntable needle.

Cone   Diaphragm part of a loudspeaker.

Counterbalance   Adjustable weight on the back of the turntable tone arm that lessens the force of the arm on the record.

CPS (cycles per second)   Vibrations per second, or hertz (Hz).

Crossover   Electrical circuit in a speaker cabinet that sends the low frequencies to the woofer, the high frequencies to the tweeter, and midfrequencies to the midrange speaker.

Cross talk   A measure of how much of one channel's sound bleeds into and can be heard on another channel.

Cue   A channel on a mixer dedicated to previewing sounds. Cue signals are not recorded (unless you choose to), just monitored.

Cue up   To prepare a sound to be heard: to find where the sound begins on a record (or whatever) and have its audio level properly adjusted so that the sound can be heard on demand.

DAT   *See* Digital audio tape.

dB (decibel)   A measure of sound volume or electrical signal strength. The bigger the number, the more signal (or sound). The smaller (more negative) the number (like –20 dB), the weaker the signal.

DBX   A noise reduction system used in recordings to remove hiss.

DC   Direct current: power you get from batteries.

Decibel   *See* dB.

Deck   A tape recorder without speakers.

Decoding   A treatment of audio signals when they are played back from a tape that restores their fidelity and dynamic range, hopefully reducing noise at the same time. The opposite of encoding.

Degauss   *See* Demagnetize.

Delay   A single repetition of a sound, slightly delayed, that makes it sound like a second instrument or voice.

Demagnetize   Remove residual magnetism from something like an audio head.

Desk stand   A microphone support that sits on a desk.

Diaphragm   A thin membrane that can vibrate back and forth either to sense sounds or to make them.

Digital   Made of 1's and 0's. A continuously variable signal (like a sound) is converted into 1's and 0's. These digits may be processed or recorded and upon playback, converted back into sound.

Digital audiotape   Recording tape on which the sounds have been converted into 1's and 0's that are recorded as data on the tape.

Digital delay   A delay system that stores the sound digitally before delaying it. *See also* Delay.

Digital recording   Conversion of the audio signal to a code of digital 1's and 0's and recording the code. By playing back the code and converting the digital signal back to analog audio, the equipment is able to reproduce higher-fidelity sound.

Direct drive Method of spinning a turntable platter by which the platter is part of the motor. The motor directly drives the capstan or turntable; no belts or idler wheels are used.

Distortion The coloring, exaggeration, or degradation of an audio signal as it is processed by an amplifier, speaker, or other audio device. *See also* Total harmonic distortion.

Dolby Dolby Laboratories trademark on a type of noise reduction. Dolby A and C are used on professional equipment; Dolby B is used on consumer equipment. If a tape is recorded and played back using Dolby, there will be less background tape hiss.

Double edit An edit made over another edit but not completely covering the sound of the beginning or end of the old edit.

Driver A loudspeaker assembly consisting of the cone and magnet but not the box.

Dub *See* Audio dub.

Duplication house Facility that duplicates audio recordings for a fee.

Dynamic microphone Mike with a coil of wire inside that converts sound vibrations into an audio signal.

Dynamic range Ability to reproduce soft sounds as well as loud ones. Wide dynamic range is preferred because it will reproduce very soft and very loud sounds.

Echo Repetition of a word or sound, like when you holler "hello" in a canyon.

Echo receive *See* Aux receive.

Echo send Mixer output that allows selected sources to have their signals sent to an outside device like an echo chamber. The resulting signal may then be sent back to the mixer (via echo return) to be mixed with other sounds.

Effects out *See* Echo send.

Effects processor Digital audio device that augments sound by adding echo, reverberation, harmonization, time compression, or flanging.

Efficiency A measure of how much sound a speaker reproduces given a certain strength signal.

Electret condenser microphone Mike with a capacitor and a power supply inside to sense sound vibrations and convert them to an electrical signal.

Electromagnet A coil of wire able to sense sound vibrations and generate an electric current or, when fed a vibrating electrical signal, move something, such as a speaker, making sound.

Elliptical stylus Preferred egg-shaped turntable needle.

Enclosure The box around a speaker.

Encoding An electronic treatment, such as Dolby and DBX, done to an audio signal during recording to make it record better with less noise.

Equalization Circuit that modifies the frequency response of signals, perhaps reducing bass, treble, or particular frequencies to make up for excessive recorded bass or treble. Phono turntable inputs are equalized to correct for weak bass and strong treble, common to all LPs.

Equalizer   An audio device that boosts or cuts a specific frequency or frequencies.

Erase head   Part of an audiotape machine that erases the tape.

Error correction   Circuitry in digital audio equipment that fills in for missing or damaged data, resulting in smooth, seamless sound.

Expander   Audio device that increases the dynamic range of sound by strengthening the loud sounds while weakening the soft sounds. Often used in conjunction with a compressor.

Fade   To move the volume control up or down during a sound. Fade up means turning the volume from off to the proper level, smoothly. The sound grows from silence to faint to normal. Fade out, or fade down, does the opposite.

Feedback   Loud screech caused when sound goes in a mike, gets amplified, comes out a speaker, and the speaker sound goes back into the mike, creating an endless loop.

Female connector   A socket with a hole or holes.

Fidelity   Accuracy or trueness of a reproduced sound.

Filter   Electronic circuit that removes certain audio frequencies from your signal.

Fish pole   Handheld boom for microphone.

Flanger   Digital audio device capable of delaying a sound slightly and changing its pitch by a continuously varying amount; capable of making spacious swoosh effects (like jet planes overhead or outer space sounds for voices).

Flat frequency response   Even reproduction of low, medium, and high frequencies.

Floor stand   A tall microphone support that sits on the floor.

Flutter   Wavering of the pitch of music (as if you were shaking a singer) due to uneven speed of a tape or record as it plays.

FM microphone   *See* Wireless microphone.

Foldback   Channel on a mixer dedicated to sounds that are not necessarily recorded (but could be) but sent elsewhere for monitoring. Music, for instance, could be sent via foldback to the dancers on stage so that they can keep in step; meanwhile you could be recording the music.

Frequency   Vibrations per second.

Frequency response   Ability of a device to reproduce a frequency. Hi-fi equipment generally has wide, even frequency response, reproducing all frequencies (within its capability) equally.

Fundamental frequency   The main frequency of a vibration (not the harmonics).

Generation   Copy of something. A copy of an original tape is second generation; a copy of that becomes third generation.

Graphic equalizer   An equalizer with slide controls to adjust certain frequencies.

Harmonics   Multiples of a fundamental frequency, usually giving the sound a flavor, color, or unique identity: overtones.

Harmonizer Digital audio device that alters the frequency of a sound going into it, perhaps harmonizing with the original sound.

Headroom The amount an audio device can be driven beyond its proper 0-VU level without distorting the sound.

Hertz or Hz Vibrations per second.

Hi fi Feature on some VCRs that allows them to record the sound with excellent fidelity, combining the sound invisibly into the picture signal.

Hi level *See* High level.

High level Strong audio signal, like that from an FM tuner, an aux output from an amplifier, or any preamplified signal.

Hiss Background noise often heard on tape.

Horn speaker Rugged, outdoor high-power, low-fidelity speaker with a hornlike flare in front of it.

Hypercardioid microphone Unidirectional microphone that is more sensitive than a cardioid in front, insensitive at the sides, and slightly sensitive at the rear.

Hz or hertz Vibrations per second.

Idler A rubber or rubber-covered wheel in a turntable or other audio device that transfers motion from a motor to a platter or capstan to make it turn.

Impedance Resistance to the flow of vibrating electrical signals.

Impedance adapter *See* Impedance matching transformer.

Impedance matching transformer Small electronic device that adapts signals of one impedance to signals of another impedance.

Insert edit A new segment recorded in the midst of an older recording, erasing and replacing the old part.

Lapel mike Mike clipped to a tie or lapel.

Lavalier mike Mike worn around the neck.

Leader Unrecordable, heavy-duty plastic ribbon at the beginning and end of a reel-to-reel or audiocassette tape that protects your recording from dirt and the rigors of threading.

LED Light-emitting diode. *See also* Peak level indicator.

Line contact stylus Highest-quality turntable needle with flattened elliptical shape.

Line level *See* High level.

Line matching transformer Small electronic circuit, often housed in an adapter, that converts three-wire balanced lines to two-wire unbalanced lines.

Line out *See* Program.

Linear track The non-hi-fi audio track on a videocassette. The track resides along the edge of the tape and is recorded linearly by a stationary audio head.

Lo level *See* Low level.

Loudness switch   Switch on a receiver that boosts the bass frequencies on soft music to make the apparent frequency response sound normal.

Low level   Weak audio signals, like those from a microphone. Low-level inputs are very sensitive, greatly amplifying weak signals.

Magnetic cartridge   Phonograph cartridge that senses vibrations with a coil of wire.

Male connector   Plug-type connector with pins that stick out.

Master   An original (as opposed to a copy) recording or the device that plays the original recording.

Master volume control   Adjusts loudness of a mixer's output, controlling all sounds at once.

Metal tape   Very high fidelity audiotape made with evaporated metal.

Microphone input   Very sensitive input on an amplifier, capable of accepting microphone and similar low-level sources.

Midrange speaker   An audio speaker that reproduces sounds in the 700–10,000-Hz range.

Mike level   *See* Low level.

Miniconnector   A small connector with a 1/8-inch plug or socket.

Mixdown   The process (or product) of playing several tracks of sound, blending the results, and rerecording the result onto another track or tracks or onto another recorder.

Mixer   Audio device that mixes sound signals and varies their levels, combining them into one (two for stereo, or more) output.

Monaural   Single-channel audio that uses one speaker for its sound.

Mono   *See* Monaural.

MTS   *See* Multichannel television sound.

Multichannel television sound   Stereo sound broadcasting for TV.

Multitrack recording   Recording sound on several independent tracks (paths) of a tape.

Music under   Music played faintly during narrations or scenes, adding drama or continuity to them.

Noise   Sounds that don't belong in your audio signal. Electronic hum and tape hiss are noise.

Noise filter   Electrical device that plugs into your AC outlet and absorbs the interference that radiates through your electrical system.

Noise reduction   Process of reducing background hiss and hum while preserving the desired sound on a recording.

Noise-canceling microphone   Microphone that rejects the din of a noisy environment. Mike must be used close to the mouth.

Normal-through   In a patch bay, the top socket automatically sends its signal to the socket directly under it when no patch cord is plugged into either socket.

Overdub   Mixing several audio signals (perhaps live sound plus several tracks already recorded on a tape) and recording the results on another track.

PA system   *See* Public address system.

Pad   Another name for an audio attenuator.

Pan pot   A volume control on stereo mixers that allows you to send a signal to the left, the right, or both channels. Turning this knob (potentiometer) will smoothly fade the signal from one channel to the other.

Parabolic microphone   Microphone system that uses a parabolic dish reflector to focus sound on a microphone.

Parametric equalizer   Audio filter that can be turned to select a frequency, then adjusted to control how much of that frequency is removed or boosted.

Patch bay   A panel having several rows of standardized sockets connected to various audio devices. Plugging a patch cable into a pair of sockets connects them so that the signal can travel from one device to another.

Pause editing   Using the pause button on a recorder to start/stop the recording process while editing.

Peak-level indicator   Light that flashes when short bursts of volume exceed a certain level.

Peak power   The maximum power an amplifier can put out or a speaker can accept in short bursts. The highest instantaneous power a device can handle.

Phase   Vibrations that add to and strengthen each other are in-phase. Out-of-phase vibrations cancel each other, weakening the signal. Microphones, sound systems, electronics, and speakers always should be positioned and wired so that their vibrations are in-phase to sound best.

Phone connector   Plug or socket with a 1/4-inch shaft or hole.

Phono connector   *See* RCA connector.

Phonograph cartridge   Part of the record player that holds the needle and senses the needle's vibrations, turning them into electrical vibrations.

Pickup pattern   A representation of how sensitive a microphone is in various directions.

Pinch roller   Large rubber roller on a tape deck that squeezes the tape against the capstan to pull it through the mechanism when the machine is playing or recording.

Pitch   The frequency of a sound. High notes on a piano have high pitch.

Platter   The spinning part of the record turntable.

Play head   Part of an audiotape machine that senses magnetism from the tape and converts it into an audio signal.

Polar diagram   A graphic representation of a microphone's sensitivity in all directions (as viewed from above).

Pot   *See* Potentiometer.

Potentiometer   Audio volume control knob or slider.

Preamplifier or preamp   Electrical device to strengthen a weak low-level electrical signal (i.e., from a microphone) up to a high level strong enough to feed the signal to other audio devices, such as amplifiers.

Program   The final master output from a mixer.

Proximity effect   Exaggerated bass sound, heard when a directional mike is too close to a performer or musical instrument.

Public address system   Audio amplifier and perhaps mikes and speakers (the rest of the system) designed primarily for presenting speech to larger audiences.

Punch-in edit   Using a recorder with this feature, the machine, at the tap of a button or footswitch, will switch immediately from play to record mode, allowing you to inset new audio on the spot.

PZM   Pressure-zone microphone, a mike attached to a plate that funnels the sound into the mike.

R-DAT   Rotary digital audiotape, recorded with a spinning head, such as those on a VCR.

RCA or phono connector   Small audio connector with a middle pin and a round outer collar, used sometimes between mixers and audiocassette decks and often between amplifiers, speakers, and phonograph turntables.

Receiver   Combination amplifier and radio tuner.

Record head   Part of an audiotape deck that records magnetism (representing sound) on the tape.

Resonate   To vibrate in sympathy with another sound. Also, sound in a room or speaker enclosure may bounce back and forth, increasing volume as the waves add together.

Reverberation   Repetition of a sound as it reflects from surfaces, scatters, and returns as a blurred continuous tone like you hear when singing in the bath or in a large tank.

Rim drive   Inexpensive method of spinning a turntable platter using an idler wheel.

RMS power   Root-mean-square, or average, constant power that an amplifier can deliver or a speaker can accept.

Roll-off   Weaker reproduction of a high or a low frequency.

Room tone   The character, color, or personality of a sound recorded in a particular room, caused by echoes and background noises in the room.

Rumble   Low rumbling sound heard when you play records on a cheap turntable or on one whose bearings are shot.

S/N ratio *See* Signal-to-noise ratio.

Sampler Digital audio device that electronically stores a sound and can play it back, often at selected pitches, at the push of a button.

Segue A fade from one sound to another. One sound fades down while the other simultaneously fades up.

Self-normalling *See* Normal-through.

Separation The degree of difference discernible between two audio channels, such as between the stereo left and right channels.

Shell The housing around an audiocassette that holds the tape.

Shock mount Mechanism that insulates a microphone from hand noises.

Shotgun microphone Extremely unidirectional microphone with a long barrel.

Signal-to-noise (S/N) ratio Numerical comparison between a signal and the equipment-generated noise added as the signal passes through the equipment. S/N ratio is measured in decibels, and the higher the number, the cleaner the sound.

Sound mix The combination of sounds that pass through a mixer and represent the final sound to be recorded or played over loudspeakers.

Sound pressure level (SPL) A measure of the pressure of a sound wave expressed in decibels. A speaker with a rating of 98-dB SPL will make 98 dBs of sound volume 1 meter in front of it when 1 watt of electrical energy is fed to the speaker.

Speaker level Very high strength audio signal, appropriate for speakers and headphones.

SPL *See* Sound pressure level.

Splicing Cutting a recording tape and attaching ends together with adhesive tape so the tape is again playable. Also a means of editing or repairing an audiotape.

Splicing block Metal block with grooves in it to guide your audiotape and your razor to make accurate edits.

Splicing tape Special adhesive tape used to join the ends of audio recording tape for continuous playback or for editing audio recordings. The adhesive doesn't bleed and goo up your machine.

Stereophonic or stereo Two-channel audio, using two speakers for its sound. Stereo plugs have two metal parts plus a ground; stereo cables have two hot wires and a ground. Stereo amplifiers have a left and a right channel, each able to carry independent sounds.

Sting A quick note or chord of music used to punctuate a scene or act as a segue between scenes.

Straight-line tracking A turntable tone arm that moves laterally rather than pivoting as the record plays.

Stylus Record needle.

Subminiature connector Tiny connector with a 3/32-inch plug or socket.

Subwoofer A large heavy-duty speaker designed for low frequencies.

Supercardioid microphone Unidirectional microphone that is more sensitive in front than a cardioid microphone and less sensitive to the sides.

Supply reel   On a reel-to-reel recorder, this is the full reel that empties as the tape plays. It contains the prerecorded tape you'll be playing or the blank tape you'll be recording on.

Sweetening   Modifying a recorded sound by playing it through an audio processing device (like an echo chamber). The improved result is then rerecorded.

Synthesizer   Electronic keyboard that creates preselected or user-modified sounds to resemble violins, pianos, organs, or other musical instruments or percussion effects.

Take-up reel   On a reel-to-reel recorder, this is the empty reel that fills as the tape plays.

THD   *See* Total harmonic distortion.

Three-way speaker system   Speaker having a three-part crossover circuit that sends the bass signals to the woofer and the high frequencies to the tweeter and the middle frequencies to the midrange speaker.

Time compressor   Digital audio device that allows you to change the speed of the sounds played through it without changing the pitch.

Tone arm   The turntable's pivoting arm that holds the needle out over the record.

Tone generator   Audio device that makes a constant audio tone signal; useful for calibrating equipment or setting volume levels.

Total harmonic distortion   A number representing the total amount of distortion or misrepresentation of a sound passing through an amplifier or speaker; how much unwanted coloration the system adds to the original sound.

Track   An independent magnetic path made on a tape, perhaps one of several, each having its own recorded message.

Tracking-force gauge   A tiny scale that measures the pressure of the needle on a record.

Turntable   Record player without an amplifier.

Tweeter   Speaker that reproduces high-frequency sounds, about 5 kHz–25 kHz.

Two-way speaker system   Speaker having a two-part crossover circuit that sends the bass and midrange signals to the woofer and sends the high and midrange frequencies to the tweeter.

Unbalanced lines   Inexpensive audio cables with one wire inside a shield.

Voice coil   Coil of wire inside a speaker that moves the speaker cone (diaphragm) when oscillating current goes through the coil.

Voice-over   Recording a narrator's voice louder than background sounds or music.

Volume unit (VU)   A measure of audio signal strength; 0 VU is the desired and maximum amount of signal a device should handle.

VU meter   Audio meter that measures (in volume units) audio signal strength and therefore recording level or sound loudness.

Watt   Measure of electrical power. One watt is roughly the power sent to the speaker of a common TV or radio in your home.

Windscreen   Foam boot that fits over a microphone to reduce the rumble of wind.

Wireless mike   FM transmitter microphone that sends the audio signal over radio waves to a receiver that tunes in the signal and sends it to your amplifier, mixer, or other destination.

Woofer   Speaker that reproduces low bass sounds, about 40–2,000 Hz.

Wow   Slow change in musical pitch as recorded music plays back. Problem often due to uneven tape speed, slippage, or a warped record.

XLR connector   Professional audio connector with a three-pin plug or socket. Takes balanced lines.

Y-adapter   Wire that splits one output into two. Allows you to feed two devices with one signal.

BIOGRAPHY

Peter Utz received both his B.S. in physics and his Ph.D. in educational technology from the University of Massachusetts. He has produced more than 500 instructional TV programs for the City University of New York and presently directs the Instructional Media Department at the County College of Morris in Randolph, New Jersey, where he also teaches video courses. He has published more than 150 articles in the fields of video, audio, computers, and instructional techniques. He has also published six books, including *Video User's Handbook*, *Complete Home Video Book*, *Do-It-Yourself Video*, *Today's Video*, and *Making Great Video*.